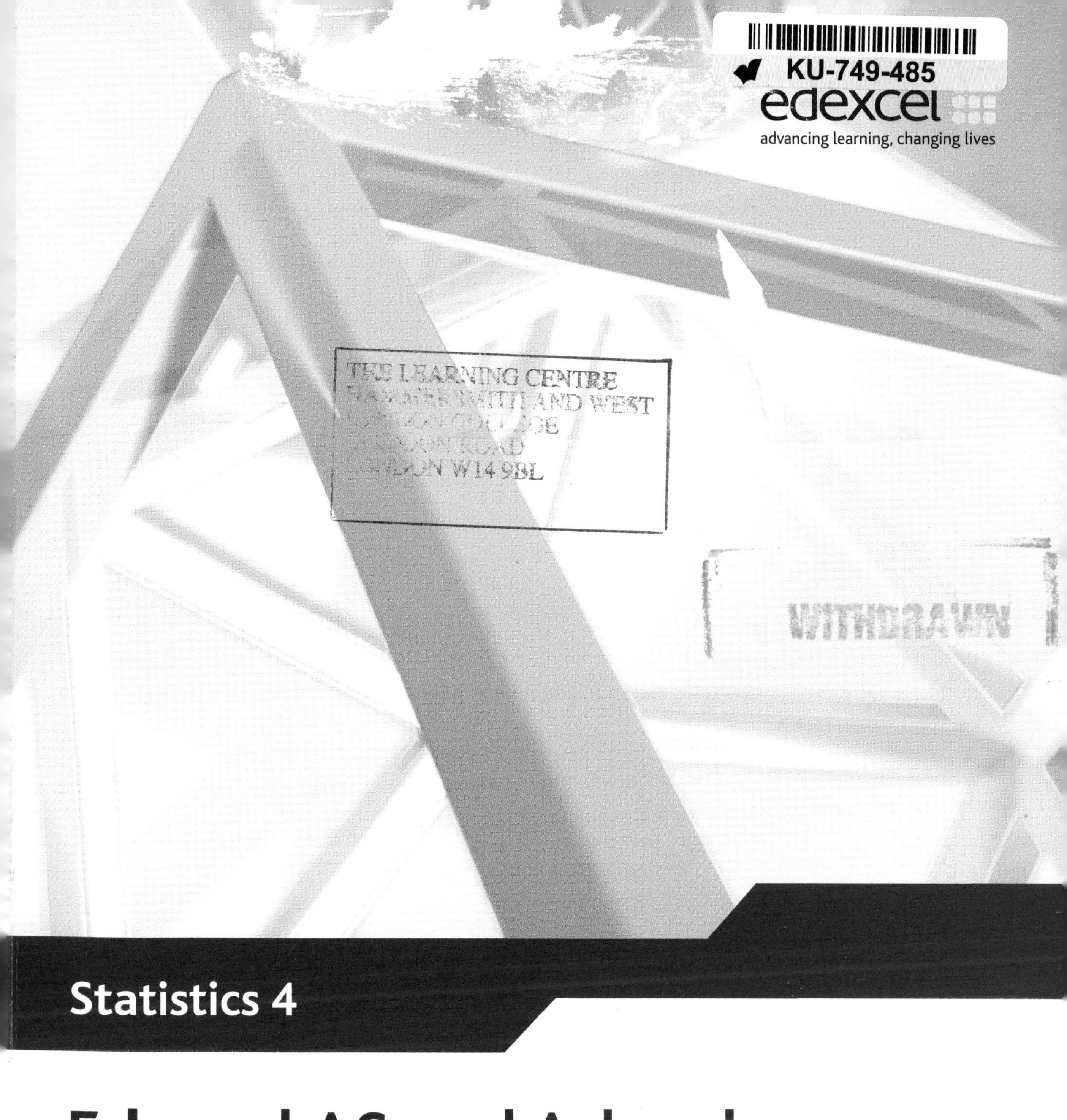

edexcel

advancing learning, changing lives

Statistics 4

Edexcel AS and A-level Modular Mathematics

Greg Attwood
Gill Dyer
Jane Dyer

Contents

About this book

This book is designed to provide you with the best preparation possible for your Edexcel S4 unit examination:

- This is Edexcel's own course for the GCE specification.
- Written by senior examiners.
- The LiveText CD-ROM in the back of the book contains even more resources to support you through the unit.

Finding your way around the book

Brief chapter overview and 'links' to underline the importance of mathematics: to the real world, to your study of further units and to your career

Every few chapters, a review exercise helps you consolidate your learning

Detailed contents list shows which parts of the S4 specification are covered in each section

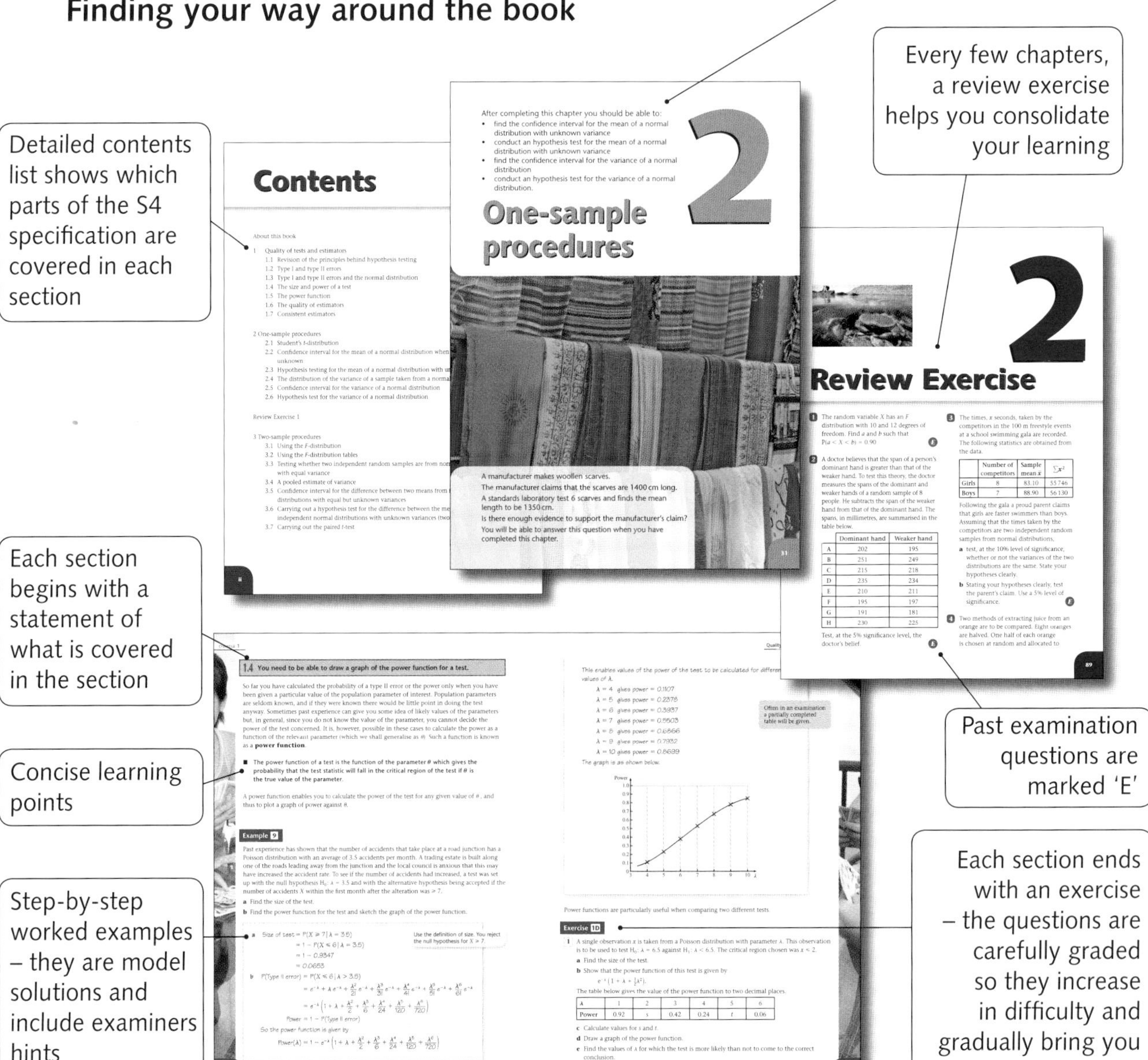

Each section begins with a statement of what is covered in the section

Concise learning points

Step-by-step worked examples – they are model solutions and include examiners hints

Past examination questions are marked 'E'

Each section ends with an exercise – the questions are carefully graded so they increase in difficulty and gradually bring you up to standard

Each chapter has a different colour scheme, to help you find the right chapter quickly

Each chapter ends with a mixed exercise and a summary of key points.

At the end of the book there is an examination-style paper.

LiveText software

The LiveText software gives you additional resources: Solutionbank and Exam café. Simply turn the pages of the electronic book to the page you need, and explore!

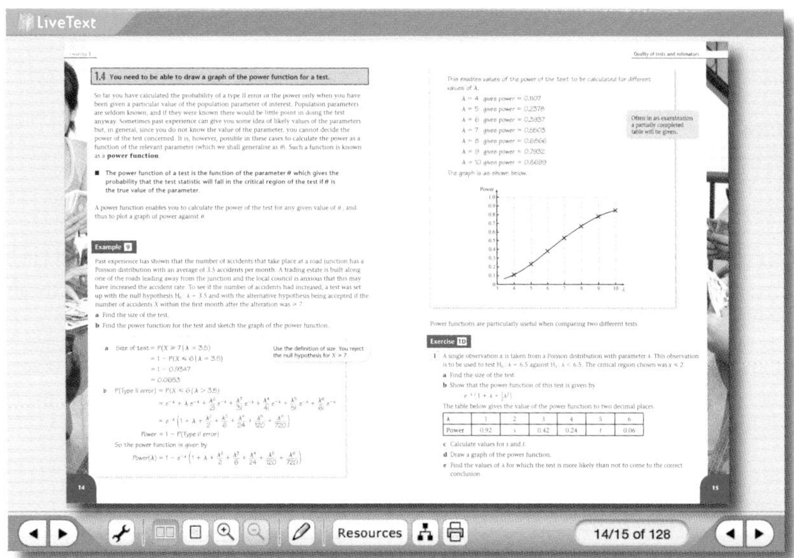

Unique Exam café feature:

- Relax and prepare – revision planner; hints and tips; common mistakes
- Refresh your memory – revision checklist; language of the examination; glossary
- Get the result! – fully worked examination-style paper with chief examiner's commentary

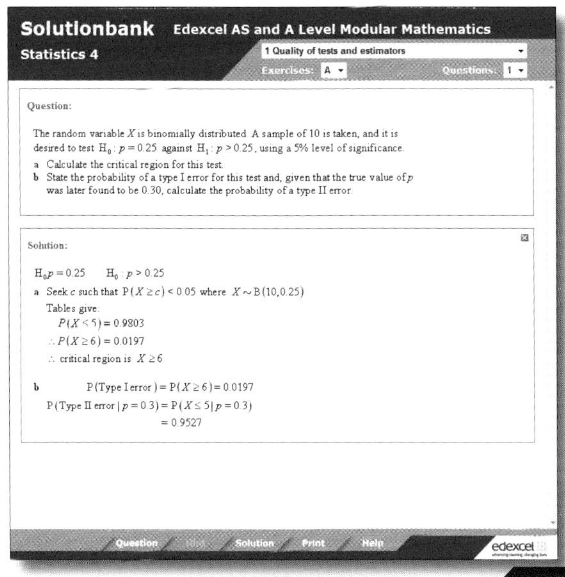

Solutionbank

- Hints and solutions to every question in the textbook
- Solutions and commentary for all review exercises and the practice examination paper

Published by Pearson Education Limited, a company incorporated in England and Wales, having its registered office at Edinburgh Gate, Harlow, Essex, CM20 2JE. Registered company number: 872828
www.pearsonschoolsandfecolleges.co.uk

Edexcel is a registered trademark of Edexcel Limited

13 12 11 10 09
10 9 8 7 6 5 4 3 2

British Library Cataloguing in Publication Data
is available from the British Library on request.

ISBN 978 0 435519 15 5

Edited by Susan Gardner
Typeset by Tech-Set Ltd, Gateshead
Illustrated by Tech-Set Ltd, Gateshead
Cover design by Christopher Howson
Picture research by Chrissie Martin
Cover photo/illustration © Edexcel
Index by Indexing Specialists (UK) Ltd
Printed in the UK by Scotprint

Acknowledgements
The author and publisher would like to thank the following individuals and organisations for permission to reproduce photographs:

Photolibrary/Asia Images RM p**1**; Shutterstock/Liveshot p**31**; Nature PL/Christopher Corteau p**60**.

Every effort has been made to contact copyright holders of material reproduced in this book. Any omissions will be rectified in subsequent printings if notice is given to the publishers.

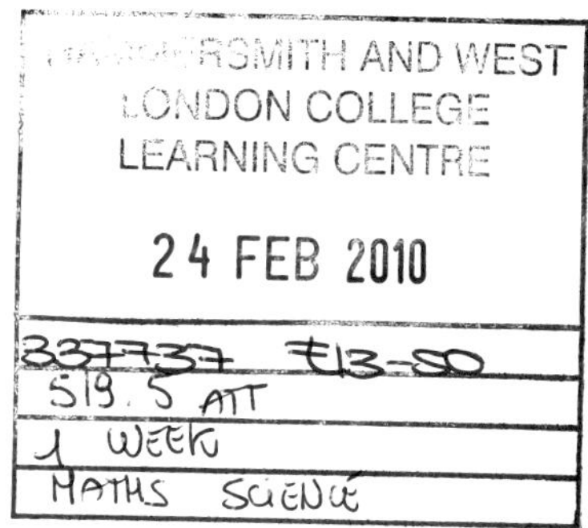

After completing this chapter you should be able to:

- explore the idea of a hypothesis test in greater depth
- find the probability of type I and type II errors
- find the power function for a hypothesis test
- assess the quality of different estimators.

Quality of tests and estimators

Testing procedures are used in a wide range of industrial processes to monitor quality and in scientific research to help direct a line of enquiry. With any of these tests there is always the risk of an error occurring. In this chapter you will learn more about these errors and see how to compare different tests.

A family of four were playing a simple game of cards. The game was one of chance so the probability of any particular person winning should have been $\frac{1}{4}$. After playing a number of games Robert complained that his younger sister Sarah must have been cheating as she kept winning. Their parents decided to carry out a proper investigation and carefully watched the next 20 games.

1.1 You need to remember the principles behind hypothesis tests.

Example 1

One rainy day during the summer holidays a family of four were playing a simple game of cards. The game was one of chance so the probability of any particular person winning should have been $\frac{1}{4}$. After playing a number of games Robert complained that his younger sister Sarah must have been cheating as she kept winning. Their parents quickly intervened and decided to carry out a proper investigation and carefully watched the next 20 games.

Find a critical region for a one-tail test using a 5% level of significance.

$H_0: p = \frac{1}{4}$ $\quad H_1: p > \frac{1}{4}$

Let X = the number of games Sarah wins out of the next 20.

So $X \sim B(20, \frac{1}{4})$

Reject H_0 if $X \geqslant c$ where $P(X \geqslant c) < 0.05$.

From tables

$P(X \leqslant 8) = 0.9591$ so $P(X \geqslant 9) = 0.0409$

$P(X \leqslant 7) = 0.8982$ so $P(X \geqslant 8) = 0.1018$

So the critical region is $X \geqslant 9$.

So if Sarah won 9 or more games there would be evidence to suggest that she was cheating.

First state the hypotheses. If Sarah is cheating then you would expect the proportion of games she wins to be more than $\frac{1}{4}$.

State the distribution of the statistic assuming H_0 is true.

Use tables to find the largest value of c.

This is the case. Sometimes 0.0409 is called the **actual significance level**.

State the critical region.

You should notice that the process of a hypothesis test is based on probability and there is always the possibility that Sarah *is* innocent but happens to have been very lucky and won 9 or more games.

The situation is similar to that of a court. The defendant is in the dock and accused of murder. The null hypothesis is that the defendant is innocent. If the jury decide to accept the null hypothesis then the defendant is free to go, if they reject the null hypothesis the defendant is sent to prison. Sometimes, though, the defendant didn't in fact commit the murder but the jury still reject the null hypothesis and an error (a miscarriage of justice) has occurred.

We shall examine the different sorts of errors that can occur in the next section.

1.2 You need to know about type I and type II errors.

In any hypothesis test or trial there is always the possibility of an error or miscarriage of justice occurring. The situation can be summarised as follows:

Notice that there are two types of error.

		Truth	
		H_0 *is* true	H_0 is false
Conclusion of test	Accept H_0	OK	Type II error
	Reject H_0	Type I error	OK

■ **A type I error is when you reject H_0 but H_0 is true.**

In the context of Example 1 this would be the case when Sarah was not cheating but she won 9 or more games and the test suggested that she *was* cheating. In the court scenario it is when an innocent person is sent to prison.

■ **A type II error is when you accept H_0 but in fact H_0 is false.**

In the context of Example 1 this would be the case where Sarah *had* in fact been cheating but she won 8 or fewer games and the test did not therefore suggest that she was cheating. In the case of the scene in court it is when a guilty person is set free.

Example 2

For the situation in Example 1

a Find the probability of a type I error.

b If in fact Sarah was cheating and $p = 0.35$, find the probability of a type II error.

a $H_0: p = \frac{1}{4}$ $\quad H_1: p > \frac{1}{4}$

From Example 1 state the hypotheses and critical region.

Critical region $X \geqslant 9$

P(Type I error) = P(Rejecting H_0 when H_0 is true)

If H_0 is true $p = 0.25$.

$= P(X \geqslant 9 \mid X \sim B(20, 0.25))$

$= 0.0409$

From tables. Notice that this is the actual significance level and it differs from the target significance level of 5%.

b P(Type II error) = P(Accept H_0 when H_0 is false)

$= P(X \leqslant 8 \mid H_0 \text{ is false})$

To accept H_0 you need $X \leqslant 8$.

Given that $p = 0.35$

The statement 'H_0 is false' does not provide a value for p so in examples of this sort a value of p is usually given.

P(Type II error) $= P(X \leqslant 8 \mid X \sim B(20, 0.35))$

$= 0.7624$

From tables.

Example 3

Accidents occurred on a stretch of motorway at an average rate of 6 per month. Many of the accidents that occurred involved vehicles skidding into the back of other vehicles. By way of a trial, a new type of road surface that is said to reduce the risk of vehicles skidding is laid on this stretch of road, and during the first month of operation 4 accidents occurred.

a Test this result to see if it gives evidence that there has been an improvement at the 5% level of significance.

b Calculate P(Type I error) for this test.

c If the true average rate of accidents occurring with this type of road surfaces was 3.5 calculate the probability of a type II error.

a You are dealing with a Poisson distribution.

Let λ = the average number of accidents in a month, and X = the number of accidents in any given month, then the hypotheses are

H_0: $\lambda = 6$ (i.e. no change)

H_1: $\lambda < 6$ (i.e. fewer accidents)

From tables $P(X \leqslant 4 \mid \lambda = 6) = 0.2851$

This is more than 5% so you do not have enough evidence to reject H_0.

The average number of accidents per month has not decreased.

b In order to reject H_0 you required a value c such that

$P(X \leqslant c \mid \lambda = 6) < 0.05$

From the table on page 104, with $\lambda = 6$:

$P(X \leqslant 2) = 0.0620$

and $P(X \leqslant 1) = 0.0174$

So the critical value c is 1, and the critical region for this test is $X \leqslant 1$.

A type I error occurs when you reject H_0 when it is true and the probability of this happening is $P(X \leqslant 1) = 0.0174$.

c A type II error occurs when you do not have sufficient evidence to reject H_0 when H_1 is true.

If $\lambda = 3.5$ then H_0 is not true. You do not have sufficient evidence to reject H_0 if $X \geqslant 2$ so

$$\begin{aligned} P(\text{Type II error} \mid \lambda = 3.5) &= P(X \geqslant 2 \mid \lambda = 3.5) \\ &= 1 - P(X \leqslant 1 \mid \lambda = 3.5) \\ &= 1 - 0.1359 \\ &= 0.8641 \end{aligned}$$

Part a is a hypothesis test for the mean of a Poisson distribution (dealt with in book S2).

Since it is a one-tailed test the conclusion should be clearly one-tailed.

You could have specified as close as possible to 5%.

This is again smaller than the 5% you were aiming for.

There is another form of the alternative hypothesis that occurs when you ask if there has been a change either up or down. In such cases a two-tailed test is used. This process is shown in the next example.

Example 4

A coin is tossed 20 times and a head is obtained on 7 occasions.

a Test to see whether or not the coin is biased.

b Calculate the probability of a type I error for this test.

c Given that the coin is biased and that this bias causes the tail to appear 3 times for each head that appears, calculate the probability of a type II error for the test.

a The hypotheses are

$H_0: p = 0.5 \qquad H_1: p \neq 0.5$

Let X = the number of heads in 20 tosses of the coin

Assuming H_0 is true then $X \sim B(20, 0.5)$

For a two-tailed test at the 5% significance level you require values c_1 and c_2 so that

$P(X \leqslant c_1) \leqslant 0.025$ and $P(X \geqslant c_2) \leqslant 0.025$

(or $P(X \leqslant c_2 - 1) \geqslant 0.975$)

From tables: $P(X \leqslant 6) = 0.0577$

and $P(X \leqslant 5) = 0.0207$

so the value of $c_1 = 5$.

Also: $P(X \geqslant 14) = 1 - P(X \leqslant 13)$

$= 1 - 0.9423$

$= 0.0577$

$P(X \geqslant 15) = 1 - P(X \leqslant 14)$

$= 1 - 0.9793$

$= 0.0207$

so the value of $c_2 = 15$.

Thus the critical region for X is $X \leqslant 5$ or $X \geqslant 15$.

As 7 falls between 5 and 15 there is insufficient evidence to reject H_0.
The coin is not biased.

b A type I error occurs when you reject H_0, and this occurs when $X \leqslant 5$ or $X \geqslant 15$.

$$\begin{aligned} P(\text{type I error}) &= P(X \leqslant 5 \mid p = 0.5) \\ &\quad + P(X \geqslant 15 \mid p = 0.5) \\ &= 0.0207 + 0.0207 \\ &= 0.0414 \end{aligned}$$

c A type II error occurs when you do not have sufficient evidence to reject H_0 when H_1 is true. You do not have evidence to reject H_0 if $X \geqslant 6$ and $X \leqslant 14$ i.e $6 \leqslant X \leqslant 14$.

$$\begin{aligned} P(\text{type II error}) &= P(6 \leqslant X \leqslant 14 \mid p = 0.25) \\ &= P(X \leqslant 14 \mid p = 0.25) \\ &\quad - P(X \leqslant 5 \mid p = 0.25) \\ &= 1 - 0.6127 \\ &= 0.3873 \end{aligned}$$

This is a test for the proportion of a binomial distribution, and since you are testing to see if the coin is biased in either direction, a two-tailed test has to be used.

The critical region will be in two parts.

Alternatively $P(X \leqslant 13) = 0.9423$ and $P(X \leqslant 14) = 0.9793$ so $c_2 - 1 = 14$ and $c_2 = 15$.

Notice that since $p = 0.5$ the two tails are symmetrical about the mean of 10 and the value of c_2 could have been inferred from that of c_1 in this case.

In this case there are two probabilities to be found and added.

Remember that
X = the number of heads and
p = the probability of getting a head.
In this case $p = 0.25$.

Exercise 1A

1 The random variable X is binomially distributed. A sample of 10 is taken, and it is desired to test $H_0: p = 0.25$ against $H_1: p > 0.25$, using a 5% level of significance.

a Calculate the critical region for this test.

b State the probability of a type I error for this test and, given that the true value of p was later found to be 0.30, calculate the probability of a type II error.

2 The random variable X is binomially distributed. A sample of 20 is taken, and it is desired to test $H_0: p = 0.30$ against $H_1: p < 0.30$, using a 1% level of significance.

a Calculate the critical region for this test.

b State the probability of a type I error for this test and, given that the true probability was later found to be 0.25, calculate the probability of a type II error.

3 The random variable X is binomially distributed. A sample of 10 is taken, and it is desired to test $H_0: p = 0.45$ against $H_1: p \neq 0.45$, using a 5% level of significance.

a Calculate the critical region for this test.

b State the probability of a type I error for this test and, given that the true probability was later found to be 0.40, calculate the probability of a type II error.

4 The random variable X has a Poisson distribution. A sample is taken, and it is desired to test $H_0: \lambda = 6$ against $H_1: \lambda > 6$, using a 5% level of significance.

a Find the critical region for this test.

b Calculate the probability of a type I error and, given that the true value of λ was later found to be 7, calculate the probability of a type II error.

5 The random variable X has a Poisson distribution. A sample is taken, and it is desired to test $H_0: \lambda = 4.5$ against $H_1: \lambda < 4.5$, using a 5% level of significance.

a Find the critical region for this test.

b Calculate the probability of a type I error and, given that the true value of λ was later found to be 3.5, calculate the probability of a type II error.

6 The random variable X has a Poisson distribution. A sample is taken, and it is desired to test $H_0: \lambda = 9$ against $H_1: \lambda \neq 9$, using a 5% level of significance.

a Find the critical region for this test.

b Calculate the probability of a type I error and, given that the true value of λ was later found to be 8, calculate the probability of a type II error.

1.3 You need to be able to find type I and type II errors using the normal distribution.

In the examples in the previous section P(Type I error), which gives the actual significance level, was not equal to the target significance level. This was due to the discrete nature of the distributions used.

■ **When a continuous distribution such as the normal distribution is used then P(Type I error) is equal to the significance level of the test.**

Example 5

Bags of sugar having a nominal weight of 1 kg are filled by a machine. From past experience it is known that the weight, X kg, of sugar in the bags is normally distributed with a standard deviation of 0.04 kg. At the beginning of each week a random sample of 10 bags is taken in order to see if the machine needs to be reset. A test is then done at the 5% significance level with $H_0: \mu = 1.00$ kg and $H_1: \mu \neq 1.00$ kg.

a Find the critical region for this test.

Assuming that the mean weight has in fact changed to 1.02 kg,

b find P(Type 1 error) and P(Type II error) for this test.

a The distribution of $\bar{X}$ is modelled by $N\left(1.0, \frac{0.04^2}{10}\right)$.

Since this is a two-tailed test you allow 2.5% at each tail.

From the tables the critical region for Z is

$Z > 1.96$ or $Z < -1.96$.

The critical values for $\bar{X}$ are given by

$$\bar{x} = 1 \pm 1.96 \times \sqrt{\frac{0.04^2}{10}}$$

$$= 0.9752 \text{ and } 1.0248$$

The critical region is found by rearranging $\left|\frac{\bar{x} - \mu}{\frac{\sigma}{\sqrt{n}}}\right| > 1.96$ for $\mu = 1.0$, $\sigma = 0.04$ and $n = 10$.

The critical region is $\bar{X} \leqslant 0.9752$ and $\bar{X} \geqslant 1.0248$

Notice once again that the critical region is in two parts.

b The P(Type I error) for this test will be the same as the significance level = 0.05, so only the P(Type II error) needs to be found.

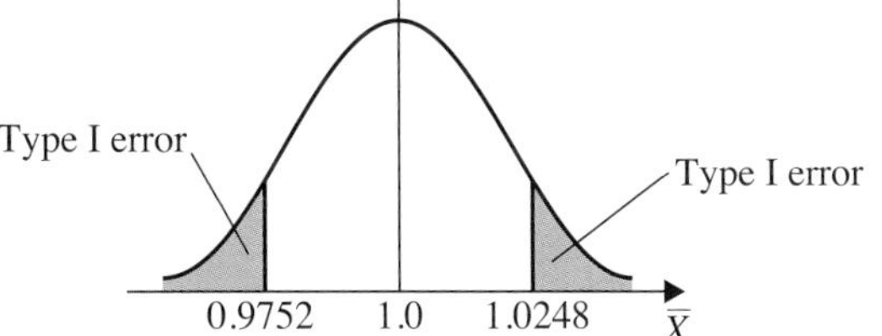

Opposite is a rough sketch showing the area to be found.

The area required lies between $\bar{X} = 0.9752$ and $\bar{X} = 1.0248$ given that $\bar{X}$ is modelled by $N\left(1.02, \frac{0.04^2}{10}\right)$.

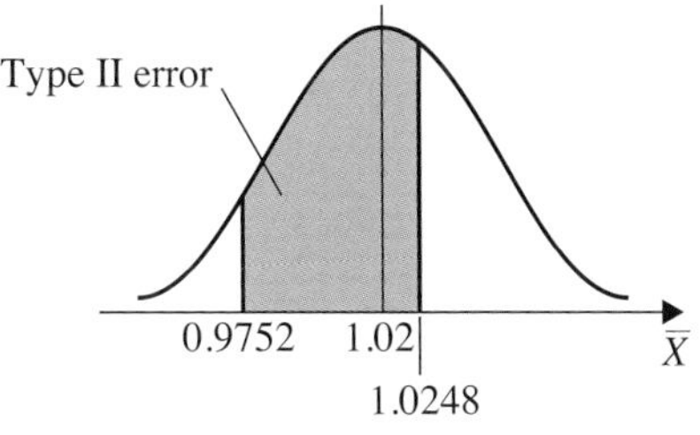

The probability of a type II error is given by

$$P(0.9752 < \bar{X} < 1.0248) = \Phi\left(\frac{1.0248 - 1.02}{\frac{0.04}{\sqrt{10}}}\right) - \Phi\left(\frac{0.9752 - 1.02}{\frac{0.04}{\sqrt{10}}}\right)$$

$\Phi(x)$ is an alternative notation for $P(Z \leqslant x)$.

$$= \Phi(0.38) - \Phi(-3.54)$$

$$= 0.6480 - (1 - 0.9998)$$

$$= 0.6478 \text{ (from tables)}$$

Calculator gives 0.6476.

Ideally we would like to keep P(Type I error) and P(Type II error) as low as possible as no one wants there to be miscarriages of justice. The following example shows something of the relationship between Type I and Type II errors.

Example 6

The weight of jam in a jar, measured in grams, is distributed normally with a mean of 150 and a standard deviation of 6. The production process occasionally leads to a change in the mean weight of jam per jar but the standard deviation remains unaltered.

The manager monitors the production process and for every new batch takes a random sample of 25 jars and weighs their contents to see if there has been any reduction in the mean weight of jam per jar.

Find the critical values for the test statistic $\overline{X}$, the mean weight of jam in a sample of 25 jars, using

a a 5% level of significance

b a 1% level of significance.

Given that the true value of μ for the new batch is in fact 147,

c find the probability of a type II error for each of the above critical regions.

a $H_0: \mu = 150$ $\quad H_1: \mu < 150$ (i.e. a one-tailed test)

$n = 25$ and $\sigma = 6$

The 5% critical region for Z is $Z \leqslant -1.6449$ so

reject H_0 if $\dfrac{\overline{X} - 150}{\frac{6}{\sqrt{25}}} \leqslant -1.6449$

That is, the critical region for $\overline{X}$ is

$$\overline{X} \leqslant \frac{6}{\sqrt{25}} \times (-1.6449) + 150$$

so $\overline{X} \leqslant 148.02612$

b The 1% critical region for Z is $Z \leqslant -2.3263$ so

reject H_0 if $\dfrac{\overline{X} - 150}{\frac{6}{\sqrt{25}}} \leqslant -2.3263$

That is, the critical region for $\overline{X}$ is

$$\overline{X} \leqslant \frac{6}{\sqrt{25}} \times (-2.3263) + 150$$

so $\overline{X} \leqslant 147.20844$

c 5% test P(Type II error) $= P(\overline{X} > 148.026\ldots \mid \mu = 147)$

$$= P\left(Z > \frac{148.026\ldots - 147}{\frac{6}{\sqrt{25}}}\right)$$

$= P(Z > 0.8551)$ [use 0.86]

$= 1 - 0.8051$

$= 0.1949$

The critical value for Z is found from tables.

State the hypotheses to define the test. You are looking for a 'reduction' in the mean so a one-tailed test is needed.

Calculator gives 0.1962.

1% test P(type II error) $= P(\overline{X} > 147.2084 \mid \mu = 147)$

$$= P\left(Z > \frac{147.2084 - 147}{\frac{6}{\sqrt{25}}}\right)$$

$= P(Z > 0.1737)$ [Use 0.17.]

$= 1 - 0.5675$

$= 0.4325$

Calculator gives 0.43105...

Notice how in this example if we try to *reduce* P(Type I error) from 5% to 1% then P(Type II error) *increases* from 0.1949 to 0.4325. A more detailed study of the interplay between these two probabilities follows later in this chapter. However, you should be aware of this phenomenon and appreciate one of the reasons why we do not always use a significance level that is very small. The value of 5% is a commonly used level and in a situation where a particular significance level is not given this value is recommended.

This does not mean that other significance levels are never used. When, for example, the results of the research are highly important and making a type I error could be very serious, a 1% significance level might be used. In other cases a significance level of 10% might be used. An alternative method of reducing the probability of a type II error is to increase the sample size but you will appreciate that more cost is linked to increased sample size.

The relationship between the probabilities of type I and type II errors can be illustrated by imagining pushing down one side of a balloon.

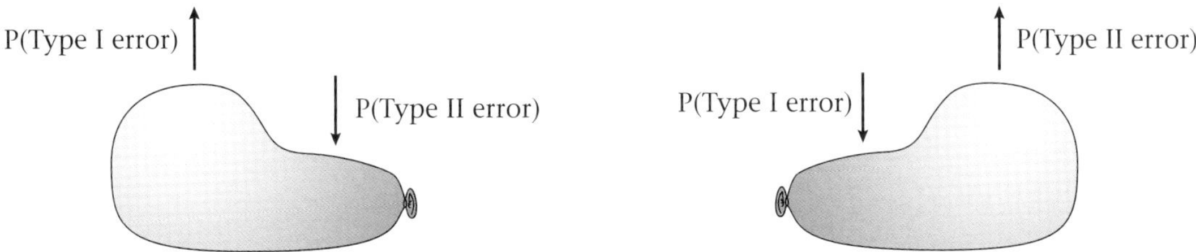

The only way to push down on both sides at once (and reduce the overall thickness) is to allow the air to move sideways. Using a larger balloon would allow you to reduce the overall thickness (this is equivalent to increasing the size of the sample n).

Exercise 1B

1 The random variable $X \sim N(\mu, 3^2)$. A random sample of 20 observations of X is taken, and the sample mean $\bar{x}$ is taken to be the test statistic. It is desired to test $H_0: \mu = 50$ against $H_1: \mu > 50$, using a 1% level of significance.

a Find the critical region for this test.

b State the probability of a type I error for this test.

Given that the true mean was later found to be 53,

c find the probability of a type II error.

2 The random variable $X \sim N(\mu, 2^2)$. A random sample of 16 observations of X is taken, and the sample mean $\bar{x}$ is taken to be the test statistic. It is desired to test $H_0: \mu = 30$ against $H_1: \mu < 30$, using a 5% level of significance.

a Find the critical region for this test.

b State the probability of a type I error for this test.

Given that the true mean was later found to be 28.5,

c find the probability of a type II error.

3 The random variable $X \sim N(\mu, 4^2)$. A random sample of 25 observations of X is taken, and the sample mean $\bar{x}$ is taken to be the test statistic. It is desired to test $H_0: \mu = 40$ against $H_1: \mu \neq 40$, using a 1% level of significance.

a Find the critical region for this test.

b State the probability of a type I error.

Given that the true mean was later found to be 42,

c find the probability of a type II error.

4 A manufacturer claims that the average outside diameter of a particular washer produced by his factory is 15 mm. The diameter is assumed to be normally distributed with a standard deviation of 1. The manufacturer decides to take a random sample of 25 washers from each day's production in order monitor any changes in the mean diameter.

a Using a significance level of 5% find the critical region to be used for this test.

Given that the average diameter had in fact increased to 15.6 mm

b find the probability that the day's production would be wrongly accepted.

5 The number of petrie dishes that a laboratory technician can deal with in one hour can be modelled by a normal distribution with mean 40 and standard deviation 8. A producer of glass pipettes claims that a new type of pipette will speed up the rate at which the technician works.

A random sample of 30 technicians tried out the new pipettes and the average number of petrie dishes they dealt with per hour $\bar{X}$ was recorded.

a Using a 5% significance level find the critical value of $\bar{X}$.

The average number of petrie dishes dealt with per hour using the new pipettes was in fact 42.

b Find the probability of making a type II error.

The manufacturer of the pipettes would like to lessen the probability of a type II error being made and recommends that the significance level be changed.

c State, giving a reason, what recommendation you would make.

1.4 You need to be able to calculate the size and power of a test.

You have already seen that a type I error occurs when the null hypothesis is rejected when it is in fact true. The probability of a type I error will be written as α and is often known as **the size of the test**.

■ **The size of a test is the probability of rejecting the null hypothesis when it is in fact true and this is equal to the probability of a type I error.**

The size of a test, as you have seen, is the actual significance level of the test and this is usually chosen before the test is carried out.

When conducting a hypothesis test you should also be interested in the probability of rejecting the null hypothesis when it is in fact untrue, as this is clearly a desirable feature of a test. The probability of rejecting the null hypothesis H_0 when it is untrue, is known as **the power of the test**.

■ **The power of a test is the probability of rejecting the null hypothesis when it is not true.**

■ **power = 1 − P(type II error)**
= P(being in the critical region when H_0 is false).

The greater the power of a test, the greater the probability of rejecting H_0 when H_0 is false. It follows that the higher the power, the better the test.

The table on page 2 can now be rewritten to show the probabilities for the different situations.

		Truth	
		H_0 *is* true	H_0 is false
Conclusion of test	Accept H_0	OK	**P(Type II error)**
	Reject H_0	**P(Type I error)**	Power = 1 − P(Type II error)

The size and power both relate to rejecting H_0.

The size relates to when H_0 is true and a type I error has been made.
The power relates to when H_0 is false and a correct decision was made.

If the power is greater than 0.5 the probability of coming to the correct conclusion (rejecting H_0 when H_0 is false), is greater than the probability of coming to the wrong conclusion (accepting H_0 when H_0 is false).

On page 9 you were told that, generally, if you increase the sample size the probability of a type II error decreases. It follows that the larger the sample size the greater the power of the test. Increasing the sample size is preferable to increasing the significance level as a way of increasing the power of a test.

Example 7

The random variable X has a binomial distribution. A random sample of size 25 was taken to test $H_0: p = 0.30$ against $H_1: p < 0.30$ using a 10% level of significance.

a Find the critical region for this test.

b Find the size of this test.

Given that $p = 0.20$

c calculate the power of this test.

a $X \sim B(25, 0.30)$

H_0 is rejected when $X \leqslant c$ where $P(X \leqslant c) \leqslant 0.10$

From tables:

$P(X \leqslant 4) = 0.0905$

$P(X \leqslant 5) = 0.1935$

So critical region is $X \leqslant 4$

b Size $=$ P(Type I error)

$= P(X \leqslant 4 | p = 0.30)$

$= 0.0905$

c If $p = 0.20$ then H_0 is false

Power $=$ P(Rejecting $H_0 | H_0$ is false i.e. $p = 0.2$)

$= P(X \leqslant 4 | p = 0.20)$

$= 0.4207$

Assuming H_0 is true.

Use tables of B(25, 0.30).

Use the definition of size and tables.

Use definition of power and tables of B(25, 0.2).

Example 8

Jam is sold in jars. The amount of jam, in grams, in a jar is normally distributed with mean μ and standard deviation 5. The manufacturer claims that μ is 106 and quality control officers will take action against the manufacturer if $\mu < 106$. A random sample of 30 jars is examined and a 5% level of significance is used.

a Find the critical region for the sample mean using this test.

Given that in fact $\mu = 102$,

b find the power of this test.

a $H_0: \mu = 106 \qquad H_1: \mu < 106$

$n = 30$ so $\overline{X} \sim N\left(106, \frac{5^2}{30}\right)$

Reject H_0 when $\overline{X} \leqslant c$

Critical region for z is $Z \leqslant -1.6449$

So $\dfrac{\overline{X} - 106}{\frac{5}{\sqrt{30}}} < -1.6449$

i.e. $\overline{X} < 104.498\ldots$

b Power $= P(\overline{X} < 104.498\ldots | \mu = 102)$

So Power $= P\left(Z < \dfrac{104.498\ldots - 102}{\frac{5}{\sqrt{30}}}\right)$

$= P(Z < 2.73688\ldots)$

$= 0.9970$

State the hypotheses clearly.

Assuming H_0 is true state the distribution of the statistic.

Use tables to find critical region for Z.

If $\mu = 102$ then $\overline{X} \sim N\left(102, \frac{5^2}{30}\right)$.

Use 2.75 in the tables.

A calculator gives 0.99689… and so in an examination answers which round to (awrt) 0.997 would be accepted.

Exercise 1C

1 The random variable $X \sim \text{N}(\mu, 3^2)$. A random sample of 25 observations of X is taken and the sample mean $\bar{x}$ is taken as the test statistic. It is desired to test $\text{H}_0: \mu = 20$ against $\text{H}_1: \mu > 20$ using a 5% significance level.

a Find the critical region for this test.

b Given that $\mu = 20.8$ find the power of this test.

2 The random variable X is a binomial distribution. A sample of 20 is taken from it. It is desired to test $\text{H}_0: p = 0.35$ against $\text{H}_1: p > 0.35$ using a 5% significance level.

a Calculate the size of this test.

b Given that $p = 0.36$ calculate the power of this test.

3 The random variable X has a Poisson distribution. A sample is taken and it is desired to test $\text{H}_0: \lambda = 4.5$ against $\text{H}_1: \lambda < 4.5$. If a 5% significance level is to be used,

a find the size of this test.

b Given that $\lambda = 4.1$ find the power of the test.

4 A manufacturer claims that a particular rivet produced in his factory has a diameter of 2 mm, and that the diameter is normally distributed with a variance of 0.004 mm^2.
A random sample of 25 rivets is taken from a day's production to test whether the mean diameter had altered, up or down, from the stated figure. A 5% significance level is to be used for this test.

If the mean diameter had in fact altered to 2.02 mm, calculate the power of this test.

5 In a binomial experiment consisting of 10 trials the random variable X represents the number of successes, and p is the probability of a success.

In a test of H_0: $p = 0.3$ against $\text{H}_1: p > 0.3$, a critical region of $x \geqslant 7$ is used.

Find the power of this test when

a $p = 0.4$,

b $p = 0.8$.

c Comment on your results. **E**

6 Explain briefly what you understand by

a a type I error,

b the size of a significance test.

A single observation is made on a random variable X, where $X \sim \text{N}(\mu, 10)$.
The observation, x, is to be used to test $\text{H}_0: \mu = 20$ against $\text{II}_1: \mu > 20$. The critical region is chosen to be $x \geqslant 25$.

c Find the size of the test. **E**

1.4 You need to be able to draw a graph of the power function for a test.

So far you have calculated the probability of a type II error or the power only when you have been given a particular value of the population parameter of interest. Population parameters are seldom known, and if they were known there would be little point in doing the test anyway. Sometimes past experience can give you some idea of likely values of the parameters but, in general, since you do not know the value of the parameter, you cannot decide the power of the test concerned. It is, however, possible in these cases to calculate the power as a function of the relevant parameter (which we shall generalise as θ). Such a function is known as a **power function**.

- **The power function of a test is the function of the parameter θ which gives the probability that the test statistic will fall in the critical region of the test if θ is the true value of the parameter.**

A power function enables you to calculate the power of the test for any given value of θ, and thus to plot a graph of power against θ.

Example 9

Past experience has shown that the number of accidents that take place at a road junction has a Poisson distribution with an average of 3.5 accidents per month. A trading estate is built along one of the roads leading away from the junction and the local council is anxious that this may have increased the accident rate. To see if the number of accidents had increased, a test was set up with the null hypothesis H_0: $\lambda = 3.5$ and with the alternative hypothesis being accepted if the number of accidents X within the first month after the alteration was $\geqslant 7$.

a Find the size of the test.

b Find the power function for the test and sketch the graph of the power function.

a Size of test $= P(X \geqslant 7 \mid \lambda = 3.5)$

$= 1 - P(X \leqslant 6 \mid \lambda = 3.5)$

$= 1 - 0.9347$

$= 0.0653$

Use the definition of size. You reject the null hypothesis for $X \geqslant 7$.

b P(Type II error) $= P(X \leqslant 6 \mid \lambda > 3.5)$

$$= e^{-\lambda} + \lambda e^{-\lambda} + \frac{\lambda^2}{2!}e^{-\lambda} + \frac{\lambda^3}{3!}e^{-\lambda} + \frac{\lambda^4}{4!}e^{-\lambda} + \frac{\lambda^5}{5!}e^{-\lambda} + \frac{\lambda^6}{6!}e^{-\lambda}$$

$$= e^{-\lambda}\left(1 + \lambda + \frac{\lambda^2}{2} + \frac{\lambda^3}{6} + \frac{\lambda^4}{24} + \frac{\lambda^5}{120} + \frac{\lambda^6}{720}\right)$$

Power $= 1 -$ P(Type II error)

So the power function is given by

$$\text{Power}(\lambda) = 1 - e^{-\lambda}\left(1 + \lambda + \frac{\lambda^2}{2} + \frac{\lambda^3}{6} + \frac{\lambda^4}{24} + \frac{\lambda^5}{120} + \frac{\lambda^6}{720}\right)$$

This enables values of the power of the test to be calculated for different values of λ.

$\lambda = 4$ gives power $= 0.1107$

$\lambda = 5$ gives power $= 0.2378$

$\lambda = 6$ gives power $= 0.3937$

$\lambda = 7$ gives power $= 0.5503$

$\lambda = 8$ gives power $= 0.6866$

$\lambda = 9$ gives power $= 0.7932$

$\lambda = 10$ gives power $= 0.8699$

The graph is as shown below.

Often in an examination a partially completed table will be given.

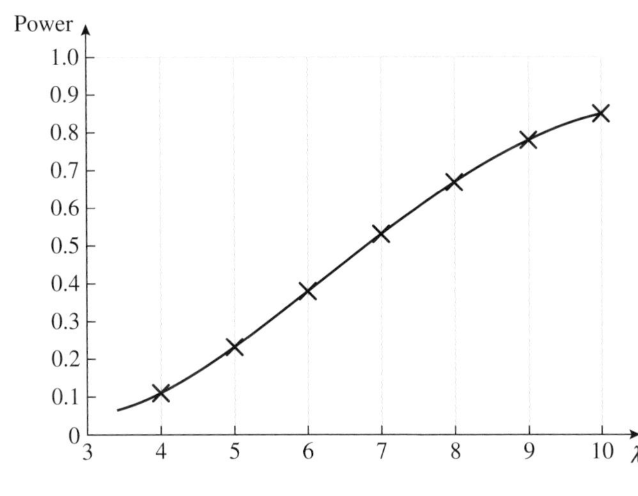

Power functions are particularly useful when comparing two different tests.

Example 10

A manufacturer of sweets supplies a mixed assortment of chocolates in a jar. He claims that 40% of the chocolates have a 'hard centre', the remainder being 'soft centred'.

A shopkeeper does not believe the manufacturer's claim and proposes to test it using the following hypotheses.

$H_0: p = 0.4 \qquad H_1: p < 0.4$

where p is the proportion of 'hard centres' in the jar. Two tests are proposed.

In test A he takes a random sample of 10 chocolates from the jar and rejects H_0 if the number of 'hard centres' is less than 2.

a Find the size of test A.

b Show that the power function of test A is given by

$$(1 - p)^{10} + 10p(1 - p)^9.$$

In test B he takes a random sample of 5 chocolates from the jar and if there are no 'hard centres' he rejects H_0, otherwise he takes a second sample of 5 chocolates and H_0 is rejected if there are no further 'hard centres' on this second occasion.

c Find the size of test B.

d Find an expression for the power function of test B.

The powers for test A and test B for various values of p are given in the table.

p	0.1	0.2	0.25	0.3	0.35
Power for test A	0.74	r	0.24	s	0.09
Power for test B	0.83	0.54	0.42	0.31	0.22

e Calculate values for r and s.

f State, giving a reason, which of the two tests the shopkeeper should use.

a Size of test $A = P(X < 2)$
$= 0.0464$

Use tables for B(10, 0.4).

b Power of test $A = P(\text{Reject } H_0 \mid p)$
$= P(X = 0 \mid p) + P(X = 1 \mid p)$
$= (1 - p)^{10} + 10p(1 - p)^9$

Use the formulae for $P(X = r)$ for a binomial distribution. The formula is in the formula booklet.

c Size of test $B = P(\text{Reject } H_0 \mid p = 0.4)$
$= P(X = 0) + \{1 - P(X = 0)\} \times P(X = 0)$
$= 0.6^5 + (1 - 0.6)^5 \times 0.6^5$
$= 0.0786$

d Power of test B = P(0 hard centres in first 5)
+ P(0 hard centres in second 5 and
> 0 hard centres in first 5)
$= P(X = 0 \mid p) + \{1 - P(X = 0 \mid p)\} \times P(X = 0 \mid p)$
$= (1 - p)^5 + \{1 - (1 - p)^5\}(1 - p)^5$
$= (1 - p)^5 \{1 + 1 - (1 - p)^5\}$
$= (1 - p)^5 \{2 - (1 - p)^5\}$
$= 2(1 - p)^5 - (1 - p)^{10}$

e Test A: $p = 0.2$ Power $= (1 - 0.2)^{10} + 10(0.2)(1 - 0.2)^9$
$= 0.38$
so $r = 0.38$

$p = 0.3$ Power $= (1 - 0.3)^{10} + 10(0.3)(1 - 0.3)^9$
so $s = 0.15$

f Power for test $B >$ Power for test A for all values of p, so he should use test B.

The reason for the final comment should be based upon the calculations of the power.

Exercise 1D

1 A single observation x is taken from a Poisson distribution with parameter λ. This observation is to be used to test $H_0: \lambda = 6.5$ against $H_1: \lambda < 6.5$. The critical region chosen was $x \leqslant 2$.

a Find the size of the test.

b Show that the power function of this test is given by

$$e^{-\lambda}\left(1 + \lambda + \tfrac{1}{2}\lambda^2\right).$$

The table below gives the value of the power function to two decimal places.

λ	1	2	3	4	5	6
Power	0.92	s	0.42	0.24	t	0.06

c Calculate values for s and t.

d Draw a graph of the power function.

e Find the values of λ for which the test is more likely than not to come to the correct conclusion.

2 In a binomial experiment consisting of 12 trials X represents the number of successes and p the probability of a success.

In a test of $H_0: p = 0.45$ against $H_1: p < 0.45$ the null hypothesis is rejected if the number of successes is 2 or less.

a Find the size of this test.

b Show that the power function for this test is given by

$$(1 - p)^{12} + 12p(1 - p)^{11} + 66p^2(1 - p)^{10}.$$

c Find the power of this test when p is 0.3.

3 In a binomial experiment consisting of 10 trials the random variable X represents the number of successes and p the probability of a success.

In a test of $H_0: p = 0.4$ against $H_1: p > 0.4$, a critical region of $x \geqslant 8$ was used.

Find the power of this test when

a $p = 0.5$

b $p = 0.8$

c Comment on your results.

4 A certain gambler always calls heads when a coin is tossed. Before he uses a coin he tests it to see whether or not it is fair and uses the following hypotheses:

$$H_0: p = \tfrac{1}{2} \qquad H_1: p < \tfrac{1}{2}$$

where p is the probability that the coin lands heads on a particular toss. Two tests are proposed.

In test A the coin is tossed 10 times and H_0 is rejected if the number of heads is 2 or fewer.

a Find the size of test A.

b Explain why the power of test A is given by

$$(1 - p)^{10} + 10p\,(1 - p)^9 + 45p^2\,(1 - p)^8.$$

In test B the coin is first tossed 5 times. If no heads result H_0 is immediately rejected. Otherwise the coin is tossed a further 5 times and H_0 is rejected if no heads appear on this second occasion.

c Find the size of test B.

d Find an expression for the power of test B in terms of p.

The power for test A and the power for test B are given in the table for various values of p.

p	0.1	0.2	0.25	0.3	0.35	0.4
Power for test A	0.9298	0.6778		0.3828		0.1673
Power for test B	0.8323	0.5480	0.4183	0.3079	0.2186	0.1495

e Find the power for test A when p is 0.25 and 0.35.

f Giving a reason, advise the gambler about which test he should use. *E*

1.6 You need to be able to assess the quality of different estimators.

In book S3 you met the idea of an unbiased estimator and learnt how to find the bias in a biased estimator.

■ **An estimator T is an unbiased estimator of the population parameter θ if $E(T) = \theta$.**

An estimator T which has the property $E(T) \neq \theta$, is called a **biased estimator.** The **bias** is simply the expected value of the estimator minus the parameter being estimated.

■ **If a statistic T is used as an estimator for a population parameter θ then the bias = $E(T) - \theta$.**

Notice that the bias will be positive if $E(T) > \theta$, but negative if $E(T) < \theta$. In practice you should always aim to use an unbiased estimator.

Example 11

The weights, in kg, of students just joining a college are normally distributed with a mean μ and variance σ^2. A random sample of 6 of these students was taken and the mean of the sample $\bar{X}$ was calculated.

a Show that $\bar{X}$ is an unbiased estimator of μ.

A second random sample of 4 of these students was taken and its mean was $\bar{Y}$.

b Show that

i $S = \dfrac{\bar{X} + \bar{Y}}{2}$ **ii** $T = \dfrac{6\bar{X} + 4\bar{Y}}{10}$

are both unbiased estimators of μ.

c Show that the estimator $U = \dfrac{\bar{X} + 2\bar{Y}}{2}$ is a biased estimator of μ.

d Find the bias of the estimator U.

a $E(\overline{X}) = \left(\dfrac{X_1 + X_2 + X_3 + X_4 + X_5 + X_6}{6}\right)$

$= \frac{1}{6}[E(X_1) + E(X_2) + E(X_3) + E(X_4) + E(X_5) + E(X_6)]$

$= \frac{1}{6}(\mu + \mu + \mu + \mu + \mu + \mu)$

$= \mu$

In book S3 you saw that for any sample of size n $E(\overline{X}) = \mu$. The proof in **a** is a special case of this result.

b i $E(S) = E\left(\dfrac{\overline{X} + \overline{Y}}{2}\right) = \frac{1}{2}E(\overline{X}) + \frac{1}{2}E(\overline{Y})$

$= \frac{1}{2}\mu + \frac{1}{2}\mu$

$= \mu$

Use the fact that $E(\overline{Y}) = \mu$ too.

ii $E(T) = E\left(\dfrac{6\overline{X} + 4\overline{Y}}{10}\right) = \frac{1}{10}[6E(\overline{X}) + 4E(\overline{Y})]$

$= \frac{1}{10}(6\mu + 4\mu)$

$= \mu$

Use the $E(aX + bY)$ formula.

c $E(U) = E\left(\dfrac{\overline{X} + 2\overline{Y}}{2}\right) = \frac{1}{2}\{E(\overline{X}) + 2E(\overline{Y})\}$

$= \frac{1}{2}(\mu + 2\mu)$

$= 1\frac{1}{2}\mu$

Since $1\frac{1}{2}\mu > \mu$, $U = \dfrac{\overline{X} + 2\overline{Y}}{2}$ is a biased estimator.

d Bias of $U = E\left(\dfrac{\overline{X} + 2\overline{Y}}{2}\right) - \mu$

$= 1\frac{1}{2}\mu - \mu$

$= \frac{1}{2}\mu$

In Example 11 there were 4 possible unbiased estimators for μ: $\overline{X}$, $\overline{Y}$, S or T. Which of these is the best to use?

In book S1 you learnt that there were two measures that could be used to describe a distribution – the mean which was a measure of location or position and the variance which was a measure of dispersion or spread. Two unbiased estimators of μ based on the sample mean $\overline{X}$ having different variances are shown opposite.

You can see from the diagram that the distribution having the smaller variance has its values clustered closer to the mean value μ, (this is what you mean when you say its variance is smaller). Thus any estimate $\bar{x}$ is likely to be closer to $E(\overline{X}) = \mu$. The estimator having the smaller variance is best.

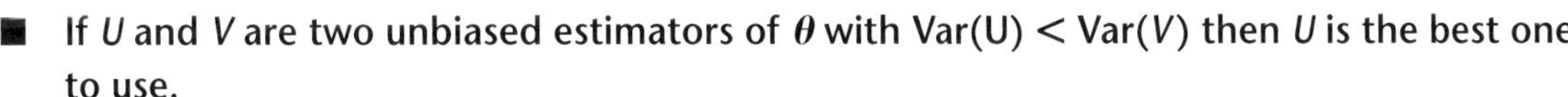

■ **If U and V are two unbiased estimators of θ with Var(U) < Var(V) then U is the best one to use.**

Example 12 (This is an extension of Example 11)

The weights, in kg, of students just joining a college are normally distributed with a mean μ and variance σ^2. A random sample of 6 of these students was taken and the mean of the sample $\overline{X}$ was calculated.

A second random sample of 4 of these students was taken and its mean was $\overline{Y}$.

The 4 statistics $\overline{X}$, $\overline{Y}$, $S = \dfrac{\overline{X} + \overline{Y}}{2}$ and $T = \dfrac{6\overline{X} + 4\overline{Y}}{10}$ are all unbiased estimators of μ. Find

a i $\text{Var}(\overline{X})$ **ii** $\text{Var}(\overline{Y})$ **iii** $\text{Var}(S)$ **iv** $\text{Var}(T)$

b Hence select the best estimator of μ.

a i $\text{Var}(\overline{X}) = \text{Var}\left(\dfrac{X_1 + X_2 + X_3 + X_4 + X_5 + X_6}{6}\right)$

$= \frac{1}{36}\{\text{Var}(X_1) + \text{Var}(X_2) + \text{Var}(X_3) + \text{Var}(X_4) + \text{Var}(X_5) + \text{Var}(X_6)\}$

$= \frac{1}{36}(\sigma^2 + \sigma^2 + \sigma^2 + \sigma^2 + \sigma^2 + \sigma^2)$

$= \frac{1}{6}\sigma^2$

In book S3 you saw that for any sample of size n Var $(\overline{X}) = \dfrac{\sigma^2}{n}$. So in part **i** $n = 6$ and in part **ii** $n = 4$.

ii Similarly $\text{Var}(\overline{Y}) = \dfrac{\sigma^2}{4}$

iii $\text{Var}(S) = \text{Var}\left(\dfrac{\overline{X} + \overline{Y}}{2}\right) = \frac{1}{4}\{\text{Var}(\overline{X}) + \text{Var}(\overline{Y})\}$

$= \frac{1}{4}\left\{\frac{1}{6}\sigma^2 + \frac{1}{4}\sigma^2\right\}$

$= \frac{5}{48}\sigma^2$

Use the Var($aX + bY$) formula.

iv $\text{Var}(T) = \text{Var}\left(\dfrac{6\overline{X} + 4\overline{Y}}{10}\right) = \frac{1}{100}\{36\text{Var}(\overline{X}) + 16\text{Var}(\overline{Y})\}$

$= \frac{1}{100}\left\{36\left(\frac{1}{6}\sigma^2\right) + 16\left(\frac{1}{4}\sigma^2\right)\right\}$

$= \frac{1}{10}\sigma^2$

b Since $\dfrac{\sigma^2}{4} > \dfrac{1}{6}\sigma^2 > \dfrac{5}{48}\sigma^2 > \dfrac{1}{10}\sigma^2$

T is the best estimator as it has the smallest variance.

Example 13

A bag is known to contain red and yellow balls. In order to find the proportion, p, of red balls in the bag a sample of m balls is taken. There were X red balls in the sample.

It was suggested that a sample of m was rather small so the balls were returned to the bag and a second sample of n balls was taken. There were Y red balls in this second sample.
The following estimators for p are proposed

$R_1 = \frac{1}{2}\left(\dfrac{X}{m} + \dfrac{2Y}{n}\right)$

$R_2 = \frac{1}{2}\left(\dfrac{X}{m} + \dfrac{Y}{n}\right)$

and $R_3 = \dfrac{X + Y}{m + n}$

a Show that R_1 is a biased estimator of p and calculate the bias of R_1.

b Show that R_2 and R_3 are unbiased estimators of p.

c Find $\text{Var}(R_2)$ and $\text{Var}(R_3)$

d If $m = 10$ and $n = 20$ state, giving reasons, which estimator you would choose.

a $$\text{E}(R_1) = \text{E}\left\{\tfrac{1}{2}\left(\frac{X}{m} + \frac{2Y}{n}\right)\right\}$$

$$= \tfrac{1}{2}\left\{\text{E}\left(\frac{X}{m}\right) + 2\text{E}\left(\frac{Y}{n}\right)\right\}$$

$$= \tfrac{1}{2}\left\{\frac{mp}{m} + 2\frac{np}{n}\right\}$$

$$= 1\tfrac{1}{2}p$$

$$\text{Bias} = \text{E}(R_1) - p = \tfrac{1}{2}p$$

You need to identify the distribution of X and the distribution of Y. $X \sim \text{B}(m, p)$ and $Y \sim \text{B}(n, p)$

Since X and Y are binomial $\text{E}(X) = mp$ and $\text{E}(Y) = np$.

b $$\text{E}(R_2) = \text{E}\left[\frac{1}{2}\left(\frac{X}{m} + \frac{Y}{n}\right)\right]$$

$$= \tfrac{1}{2}\left\{\frac{1}{m}\text{E}(X) + \frac{1}{n}\text{E}(Y)\right\}$$

$$= \tfrac{1}{2}\left(\frac{mp}{m} + \frac{np}{n}\right)$$

$$= p$$

So R_2 is an unbiased estimator of p

$$\text{E}(R_3) = \frac{1}{m+n}\{\text{E}(X) + \text{E}(Y)\}$$

$$= \frac{1}{m+n}(mp + np)$$

$$= p$$

So R_3 is an unbiased estimator of p

c $$\text{Var}(R_2) = \text{Var}\left\{\tfrac{1}{2}\left(\frac{X}{m} + \frac{Y}{n}\right)\right\}$$

$$= \tfrac{1}{4}\left\{\frac{1}{m^2}\text{Var}(X) + \frac{1}{n^2}\text{Var}(Y)\right\}$$

$$= \tfrac{1}{4}\left\{\frac{1}{m^2}mp(1-p) + \frac{1}{n^2}np(1-p)\right\}$$

$$= \tfrac{1}{4}p(1-p)\left(\frac{m+n}{mn}\right) = \tfrac{1}{4}p(1-p)\left(\frac{m+n}{mn}\right)$$

$$\text{Var}(R_3) = \frac{1}{(m+n)^2}\{\text{Var}(X) + \text{Var}(Y)\}$$

$$= \frac{1}{(m+n)^2}\{mp(1-p) + np(1-p)\}$$

$$= \frac{(m+n)p(1-p)}{(m+n)^2} = \frac{1}{m+n}p(1-p)$$

Use the $\text{Var}(aX + bY)$ formula.

Since X and Y have binomial distributions then $\text{Var}(X) = mp(1-p)$ and $\text{Var}(Y) = np(1-p)$.

d Since R_1 is biased you only need to consider R_2 and R_3.

If $m = 10$ and $n = 20$

$$\text{Var}(R_2) = \tfrac{1}{4}p(1-p)\left(\frac{20+10}{200}\right) = \tfrac{3}{80}p(1-p)$$

$$\text{Var}(R_3) = \frac{1}{m+n}p(1-p) = \tfrac{1}{30}p(1-p)$$

$\text{Var}(R_3) < \text{Var}(R_2)$ so R_3 is the better estimator.

An unbiased estimator is usually chosen in preference to a biased one.

Exercise 1E

1 A random sample of size 3 is taken without replacement, from a population with mean μ and variance σ^2. Two unbiased estimators of the mean of the population are $\hat{\mu}_1 = \frac{1}{3}(X_1 + X_2 + X_3)$ and $\hat{\mu}_2 = \frac{1}{4}(X_1 + 2X_2 + X_3)$.

a Calculate $\text{Var}(\hat{\mu}_1)$ and $\text{Var}(\hat{\mu}_2)$.

b Hence state, giving a reason, which estimator you would recommend. 

2 If X_1, X_2, X_3, is a random sample from a population with mean μ and variance σ^2, find which of the following estimators of μ are unbiased. If any are biased find an expression for the bias.

a $\frac{1}{8}X_1 + \frac{3}{8}X_2 + \frac{1}{2}X_3$ **b** $\frac{1}{4}X_1 + \frac{1}{2}X_2$ **c** $\frac{1}{3}X_1 + \frac{2}{3}X_2$

d $\frac{1}{3}(X_1 + X_2 + X_3)$ **e** $\frac{1}{5}X_1 + \frac{2}{5}X_2 + \frac{3}{5}X_3$

3 Find which one of the estimators in question 2 is the best.

4 A uniform distribution on the interval $[0, a]$ has a mean of $\frac{a}{2}$, and a variance of $\frac{a^2}{12}$.

Three single samples X_1, X_2 and X_3 are taken from this distribution, and are to be used to estimate a. The following estimators are proposed.

i $X_1 + X_2 + X_3$ **ii** $\frac{2}{3}(X_1 + X_2 + X_3)$ **iii** $2(X_1 + 2X_2 + X_3)$

a Determine the bias, if any of each of these estimators.

b Find the variance of each of these estimators.

c State, giving reasons, which of these estimators you would use.

d If $x_1 = 2$, $x_2 = 2.5$ and $x_3 = 3.2$, calculate the best estimate of a.

5 A bag contains 100 counters of which an unknown number m are blue. It is known that $2 \leqslant m \leqslant 98$. Two discs are drawn simultaneously from the bag and the number n of blue ones counted. It is desired to estimate m by $\hat{m} = cn$ where c is an unknown constant. Find the value of c given that the estimate is unbiased.

6 A sample of size n is taken from a population with a mean of μ and variance of σ^2.

a Show that the sample mean $\bar{X}$ is an unbiased estimator of μ.

b Show that as n increases $\text{Var}(\bar{X})$ decreases.

c Show that $S^2 = \dfrac{\sum X_i^2 - n\bar{X}^2}{n-1}$ is an unbiased estimator of σ^2, but that $T = \dfrac{\sum X_i^2 - n\bar{X}^2}{n}$ is a biased estimator of σ^2.

7 A six-sided die has some of its faces showing the number 0 and the rest showing the number 1 so that p is the probability of getting a 1 when the die is thrown and q is the probability of getting a 0. If the random variable X is the value showing when the die is rolled,

a find $\text{E}(X)$ and $\text{Var}(X)$.

A random sample is now taken by rolling the die three times in order to get an estimate for p.

b Show that if $a_1X_1 + a_2X_2 + a_3X_3$ is to be an unbiased estimator of p then $a_1 + a_2 + a_3 = 1$.

c Find the variance of this estimator.

The following estimators of p are proposed.

i $\frac{1}{5}X_1 + \frac{2}{5}X_2 + \frac{2}{5}X_3$ **ii** $\frac{1}{4}X_1 + \frac{3}{8}X_2 + \frac{1}{4}X_3$ **iii** $\frac{4}{9}X_1 + \frac{5}{9}X_3$

d Find which of these is the best unbiased estimator.

1.7 You need to know about consistent estimators.

In book S3 (and question 6 of Exercise 1E) you saw that the sample mean $\bar{X}$ was an unbiased estimator of μ, and that as n increases the variance of this estimator decreases. This is a property that makes $\bar{X}$ a very useful estimator of μ.

You saw that if $X \sim \text{N}(\mu, \sigma^2)$ then $\text{E}(\bar{X}) = \mu$ and $\text{Var}(\bar{X}) = \frac{\sigma^2}{n}$.

By increasing the sample size it is possible to make sure that the values of any estimates should be closer to the value of μ. If an unbiased estimator has the property that its variance approaches zero as n approaches infinity it is known as a **consistent** estimator. Sometimes an estimator Y, may be **asymptotically unbiased** as an estimator for θ. This means that $\text{E}(Y) \to \theta$ as $n \to \infty$. Such an estimator is also called consistent if $\text{Var}(Y) \to 0$ as $n \to \infty$.

- **If T is an estimator for an unknown parameter θ, then T is a consistent estimator for θ if $\text{E}(T) = \theta$ (or $\text{E}(T) \to \theta$ as $n \to \infty$) and $\text{Var}(T) \to 0$ as $n \to \infty$, where n is the size of the sample from which T is obtained.**

Example 14

A sample of size n is taken from a population that has a mean of μ and a variance of σ^2.

Show that the sample mean $\bar{X}$ is a consistent estimator of μ.

From S3: $\text{E}(\bar{X}) = \mu$ so $\bar{X}$ is an unbiased estimator of μ.

Also $\text{Var}(\bar{X}) = \frac{\sigma^2}{n}$.

As $n \to \infty$, $\frac{\sigma^2}{n} \to 0$ so $\bar{X}$ is a consistent estimator of μ.

The results $\text{E}(\bar{X}) = \mu$ and $\text{Var}(\bar{X}) = \frac{\sigma^2}{n}$ should be known and may be quoted.

Example 15

From a binomial population in which the proportion of successes is p, a random sample of size n is taken and the number of successes X is recorded. The proportion of successes in the sample R is used as an estimator for p. Show that R is a consistent estimator of p.

$$\begin{aligned}
E(R) &= E\left(\frac{X}{n}\right)\\
&= \frac{1}{n}E(X)\\
&= \frac{1}{n}(np)\\
&= p
\end{aligned}$$

so R is an unbiased estimator of p

$$\begin{aligned}
Var(R) &= Var\left(\frac{X}{n}\right)\\
&= \frac{1}{n^2}Var(X)\\
&= \frac{1}{n^2}(np(1-p))\\
&= \frac{1}{n}p(1-p) = \frac{1}{n}p(1-p)
\end{aligned}$$

Thus as $n \to \infty$, $Var(R) \to 0$ and R is a consistent estimator.

First you must show that R is an unbiased estimator of p.

Recall from S2 that if $X \sim B(n, p)$ then $E(X) = np$ and $Var(X) = np(1 - p)$.

Example 16

The random variable $X \sim U[0, a]$, where a is a positive constant. A random sample $X_1, X_2, \ldots, X_n$ is taken and the statistic $M = \text{Max}\{X_1, X_2, \ldots, X_n\}$ is calculated. The sampling distribution of M has probability density function given by

$$f(x) = \begin{cases} \dfrac{nx^{n-1}}{a^n} & 0 \leqslant x \leqslant a \\ 0 & \text{otherwise} \end{cases}$$

a Show that M is a biased estimator of a and find the bias.

b Show that $Var(M) = \dfrac{na^2}{(n+1)^2(n+2)}$

c Find a consistent estimator for a of the form kM, where k is a constant ($k \neq 1$).

A random sample of 5 values of x is 7, 11, 5, 9, 8.

d Calculate an unbiased estimate of a.

a
$$\begin{aligned}
E(M) &= \int_0^a x \cdot \frac{nx^{n-1}}{a^n}\,dx\\
&= \int_0^a \frac{nx^n}{a^n}\,dx = \left[\frac{nx^{n+1}}{(n+1)a^n}\right]_0^a\\
&= \left(\frac{na^{n+1}}{(n+1)a^n}\right) - (0) = \frac{na}{n+1}
\end{aligned}$$

So M is a biased estimator of a.

Use the definition of the mean for continuous distributions from S2.

Integrate and evaluate in the usual way.

$$\text{Bias} = E(M) - a = \frac{na}{n+1} - a = -\frac{a}{n+1}$$

b $$\text{Var}(M) = \int_0^a x^2 \cdot \frac{nx^{n-1}}{a^n}\,dx - \left(\frac{na}{n+1}\right)^2$$

Use the definition from S2.

$$= \left[\frac{nx^{n+2}}{(n+2)a^n}\right]_0^a - \frac{n^2a^2}{(n+1)^2}$$

$$= \frac{na^2[n^2 + 2n + 1 - n^2 - 2n]}{(n+2)(n+1)^2} = \frac{na^2}{(n+2)(n+1)^2}$$

c From part **a** $E(M) = \dfrac{na}{n+1}$

So an estimator $Q = \dfrac{n+1}{n}M$

has $E(Q) = \dfrac{n+1}{n}E(M) = \dfrac{(n+1)}{n} \times \dfrac{na}{(n+1)} = a$

Use the result from part **a** to find a value for k such that Q will be an unbiased estimator of a.

So Q is an unbiased estimator of a.

$$\text{Var}(Q) = \left(\frac{n+1}{n}\right)^2 \text{Var}(M)$$

$$= \left(\frac{n+1}{n}\right)^2 \times \frac{na^2}{(n+1)^2(n+2)}$$

$$= \frac{a^2}{n(n+2)}$$

Now you need Var(Q) and will have to use $\text{Var}(Q) = k^2\,\text{Var}(M)$ and part **b.**

As $n \to \infty$, $\text{Var}(Q) \to 0$

So $Q = \dfrac{n+1}{n}M$ is a consistent estimator of a.

Now test that Var(Q) tends to zero as n tends to infinity.

d $n = 5$ and $\max\{x\} = 11$

So an estimate of a is $\frac{6}{5} \times 11 = 13.2$.

Exercise 1F

1 A biased die has probability of a six equal to p. The die is rolled n times and the number of sixes recorded. The die is then rolled a further n times and the number of sixes recorded. The proportion of the $2n$ rolls that were sixes is called R.

a Show that R is a consistent estimator of p.

The die is rolled a total of 50 times and 18 sixes are recorded.

b Find an estimate of p.

2 The continuous random variable $X \sim U[0, a]$.

a Show that $2\bar{X}$ is an unbiased estimator of a.

b Determine whether or not $2\bar{X}$ is a consistent estimator of a.

3 Using the information and results from Example 16 show that M is a consistent estimator of a.

4 If a random sample $X_1, X_2, X_3, \ldots, X_n$, is taken from a population with mean μ and standard deviation σ. Show that both

$$\frac{1}{n}(X_1 + X_2 + \ldots + X_{n-1} + X_n), \text{ and}$$

$$2\frac{(nX_1 + (n-1)X_2 + \ldots + 2X_{n-1} + 1X_n)}{n(n+1)}$$

are unbiased and consistent estimators for μ.

You may use

$$\sum_{r=1}^{n} r = \tfrac{1}{2}n(n+1) \text{ and}$$

$$\sum_{r=1}^{n} r^2 = \tfrac{1}{6}n(n+1)(2n+1)$$

5 The random variable $X \sim \mathrm{U}[0, a]$.

a Show that $\mathrm{E}(X^n) = \dfrac{a^n}{n+1}$

A random sample of 3 readings is taken from X and the statistic $S = X_1^2 + X_2^2 + X_3^2$ is calculated.

b Show that S is an unbiased estimator of a^2.

c Show that $\mathrm{Var}(X^2) = \frac{4}{45}a^4$

A random sample of size n is taken of X.

d Show that $T = \dfrac{3}{n}(X_1^2 + X_2^2 + \ldots + X_n^2)$ is a consistent estimator of a^2.

6 When a die is rolled the probability of obtaining a six is an unknown constant p. In order to estimate p the die is rolled n times and the number, X, of sixes is recorded. A second trial is then done with the die being rolled the same number of times, and the number of sixes Y is again recorded. Show that

a $\hat{p}_1 = \dfrac{3\bar{X} + 4\bar{Y}}{7n}$, and $\hat{p}_2 = \dfrac{\bar{X} + \bar{Y}}{2n}$, are unbiased and consistent estimators of p.

b State, giving reasons, which of the two estimators is the better one.

Mixed exercise 1G

1 The random variable X is binomially distributed. A sample of 15 observations is taken and it is desired to test $\mathrm{H}_0: p = 0.35$ against $\mathrm{H}_1: p > 0.35$ using a 5% significance level.

a Find the critical region for this test.

b State the probability of making a type I error for this test.

The true value of p was found later to be 0.5.

c Calculate the power of this test.

2 The random variable X has a Poisson distribution. A sample is taken and it is desired to test $\mathrm{H}_0: \lambda = 3.5$ against $\mathrm{H}_1: \lambda < 3.5$ using a 5% significance level.

a Find the critical region for this test.

b State the probability of committing a type I error for this test.

Given that the true value of λ is 3.0

c find the power of this test.

3 The random variable $X \sim \mathrm{N}(\mu, 9)$. A random sample of 18 observations is taken, and it is desired to test $\mathrm{H}_0: \mu = 8$ against $\mathrm{H}_1: \mu \neq 8$, at the 5% significance level. The test statistic to be used is

$$Z = \frac{\bar{X} - \mu}{\frac{\sigma}{\sqrt{n}}}$$

a Find the critical region for this test.

b State the probability of a type I error for this test.

Given that μ was later found to be 7

c find the probability of making a type II error.

d State the power of this test.

4 A single observation, x, is taken from a Poisson distribution with parameter λ. The observation is used to test $H_0: \lambda = 4.5$ against $H_1: \lambda > 4.5$. The critical region chosen for this test was $x \geqslant 8$.

a Find the size of this test.

b The table below gives the power of the test for different values of λ.

λ	1	2	3	4	5	6	7	8	9	10
Power	0	0.0011	0.0019	r	0.1334	s	0.4013	0.5470	t	0.7798

i Find values for r, s and t. **ii** Using graph paper, plot the power function against λ.

5 In a binomial experiment consisting of 15 trials X represents the number of successes and p the probability of success.

In a test of $H_0: p = 0.45$ against $H_1: p < 0.45$ the critical region for the test was $X \leqslant 3$.

a Find the size of the test.

b Use the table of the binomial cumulative distribution function to complete the table given below.

p	0.1	0.2	0.3	0.4	0.5
Power	0.944	s	0.2969	t	0.0176

c Draw the graph of the power function for this test

6 A bag contains 25 balls of which an unknown number, m, are coloured red ($3 < m \leqslant 22$). Two of the balls are drawn from the bag and the number of red balls, X, is noted. It is desired to estimate m by $\hat{m} = cX$.

a Calculate a value for c if the estimate is to be unbiased.

The balls are replaced and a second draw is made and the number of red balls, Y, is noted.

b Write down $E(Y)$.

c Show that $Z = (5X + 7.5Y)$ is an unbiased estimator of m.

7 A bag contains 25 balls of which an unknown number, m, are green, ($4 < m \leqslant 21$).

Three balls are drawn from the bag and the number, X, of green balls is recorded. The balls are replaced and four balls are drawn with the number, Y, of green balls noted.

Three estimators of p, the probability of getting a green ball, are proposed

i $\dfrac{X + Y}{7}$ **ii** $\dfrac{3X + 4Y}{25}$ **iii** $\dfrac{4X + 3Y}{24}$

a Show that all three are unbiased estimators of p.

b Find which is the best estimator.

8 A company buys rope from Bindings Ltd and it is known that the number of faults per 100 m of their rope follows a Poisson distribution with mean 2. The company is offered 100 m of rope by Tieup, a newly established rope manufacturer. The company is concerned that the rope from Tieup might be of poor quality.

a Write down the null and alternative hypotheses appropriate for testing that rope from Tieup is in fact as reliable as that from Bindings Ltd.

b Derive a critical region to test your null hypothesis with a size of approximately 0.05.

c Calculate the power of this test if rope from Tieup contains an average of 4 faults per 100 m. **E**

9 The number of faulty garments produced per day by machinists in a clothing factory has a Poisson distribution with mean 2. A new machinist is trained and the number of faulty garments made in one day by the new machinist is counted.

a Write down the appropriate null and alternative hypotheses involved in testing the theory that the new machinist is at least as reliable as the other machinists.

b Derive a critical region, of size approximately 0.05, to test the null hypothesis.

c Calculate the power of this test if the new machinist produces an average of 3 faulty garments per day.

The number of faulty garments produced by the new machinist over three randomly selected days is counted.

d Derive a critical region, of approximately the same size as in part **b**, to test the null hypothesis.

e Calculate the power of this test if the machinist produces an average of 3 faulty garments per day.

f Comment briefly on the difference between the two tests. **E**

10 A single observation, x, is to be taken from a Poisson distribution with parameter μ. This observation is to be used to test $H_0: \mu = 6$ against $H_1: \mu < 6$. The critical region is chosen to be $x \leqslant 2$.

a Find the size of the critical region.

b Show that the power function for this test is given by

$$\tfrac{1}{2}e^{-\mu}(2 + 2\mu + \mu^2)$$

The table below gives the values of the power function to 2 decimal places.

μ	1.0	1.5	2.0	4.0	5.0	6.0	7.0
Power	0.92	0.81	s	0.24	t	0.06	0.03

c Calculate the values of s and t.

d Draw a graph of the power function.

e Find the range of values of μ for which the power of this test is greater than 0.8. **E**

11 The random variable X has the following distribution:

x	0	1
$P(X = x)$	q	p

a Find E(X) and Var(X).

A random sample X_1, X_2, X_3, is taken from the distribution in order to estimate p.

b Find the condition which must be satisfied by the constants a_1, a_2, a_3, if $a_1X_1 + a_2X_2 + a_3X_3$ is to be an unbiased estimator of p.

c Find the variance of this estimator.

The following estimators are proposed:

i $\frac{1}{6}X_1 + \frac{1}{3}X_2 + \frac{1}{2}X_3$ **ii** $\frac{1}{3}X_1 + \frac{1}{6}X_2 + \frac{5}{12}X_3$ **iii** $\frac{7}{12}X_1 + \frac{5}{12}X_2$

d Of these three estimators, find the best unbiased estimator. **E**

12 Two sets of binomial trials were carried out and in both sets the probability of success is p. In the first set there were X successes out of n trials and in the second set there were Y successes out of m trials.

Possible estimators for p are $\hat{p}_1 = \frac{1}{2}\left(\frac{X}{n} + \frac{Y}{m}\right)$ and $\hat{p}_2 = \frac{X + Y}{n + m}$

a Show that both $\hat{p}_1$ and $\hat{p}_2$ are unbiased estimators of p.

b Find the variances of $\hat{p}_1$ and $\hat{p}_2$

c If $n = 10$ and $m = 20$ state, giving a reason, which estimator you would use. **E**

13 (In this question max (a, b) = the greater of the two values a and b.)
A palaeontologist was attempting to estimate the length of time, T, in years, during which a small herbivorous dinosaur existed on Earth. He believed from other evidence that the earliest existence of the animal had been at the start of the Jurassic period.

Two examples of the animal had been discovered in the fossil record, at times t_1 and t_2 after the start of the Jurassic period. His model assumed that these times were values of two independent random variables T_1 and T_2 each having a continuous uniform distribution on the interval $[0, \tau]$. He considered three estimators for τ:

$$\tau_1 = T_1 + T_2, \qquad \tau_2 = \sqrt{3}\,|T_2 - T_1|, \qquad \tau_3 = 1.5\max(T_1, T_2)$$

He used appropriate probability theory and calculated the results shown in the table.

Variable	Expectation	Variance
T_1	$\frac{\tau}{2}$	$\frac{\tau^2}{12}$
$\lvert T_2 - T_1 \rvert$	$\frac{\tau}{3}$	$\frac{\tau^2}{18}$
$\max(T_1, T_2)$	$\frac{2\tau}{3}$	$\frac{\tau^2}{18}$

Using these results,

a determine the bias of each of his estimators,

b find the variance of each of his estimators.

Using your results from **a** and **b**, state, giving a reason,

c which estimator is the best of the three,

d which estimator is the worst. **E**

Summary of key points

1 A **type I error** occurs when H_0 is rejected when it is in fact true.

2 A **type II error** occurs when H_0 is accepted when it is in fact false.

3 **P(Type I error)** = the actual **significance level** of a test

4 The **size** of a test = P(Type I error of that test)

5 The **power** of a test = P(rejecting H_0 when it is false)

6 The **power** of a test = **1 − P(Type II error of that test)**

7 A statistic Y is an **unbiased estimator** of a parameter θ if $\mathbf{E(Y) = \theta}$.

8 If there are more than 1 unbiased estimators then the best one is the one with the smaller variance.

9 The bias = $E(Y) - \theta$.

10 A statistic Y is a **consistent estimator** of a parameter θ if it is

i an **unbiased** (or asymptotically unbiased) estimator of θ

and **ii** $\mathbf{Var(Y) \to 0}$ as $n \to \infty$

where n is the size of the sample from which Y is obtained.

After completing this chapter you should be able to:

- find the confidence interval for the mean of a normal distribution with unknown variance
- conduct an hypothesis test for the mean of a normal distribution with unknown variance
- find the confidence interval for the variance of a normal distribution
- conduct an hypothesis test for the variance of a normal distribution.

One-sample procedures

A manufacturer makes woollen scarves.

The manufacturer claims that the scarves are 1400 cm long.

A standards laboratory test 6 scarves and finds the mean length to be 1350 cm.

Is there enough evidence to support the manufacturer's claim?

You will be able to answer this question when you have completed this chapter.

2.1 You need to know about student's *t*-distribution.

In book S3 you saw that if n observations were taken from a normal distribution with mean μ, and variance σ^2, the sample mean $\bar{X}$ followed a $N\left(\mu, \frac{\sigma^2}{n}\right)$ distribution, and that $Z = \frac{(\bar{X} - \mu)}{\frac{\sigma}{\sqrt{n}}}$ followed a $N(0, 1^2)$ distribution.

If σ was unknown then S, where S^2 was an **unbiased estimator** of σ, was used.

Then **providing *n* was large,**

$$\frac{(\bar{X} - \mu)}{\frac{S}{\sqrt{n}}} \approx N(0, 1^2)$$

Remember that $S^2 = \frac{\sum X^2 - n\bar{X}^2}{n-1}$

$$= \frac{1}{n-1}\left\{\sum X^2 - \frac{(\sum X)^2}{n}\right\}$$

$$= \frac{S_{xx}}{(n-1)}$$

However, if ***n* is small**, S is unlikely to be very close to σ and $\frac{(\bar{X} - \mu)}{\frac{S}{\sqrt{n}}}$ can no longer be modelled by the normal distribution $N(0, 1^2)$.

When n is small we usually use the symbol t to denote the quantity $\frac{(\bar{X} - \mu)}{\frac{S}{\sqrt{n}}}$.

It is usual to use t for both the distribution and for a particular value of it. Some books use T for the random variable and t for a particular value of it.

- **If a random sample $X_1, X_2, \ldots, X_n$ is selected from a normal distribution with mean μ and unknown variance σ^2 then**

  $$t = \frac{(\bar{X} - \mu)}{\frac{S}{\sqrt{n}}} \text{ has a } t_{n-1}\text{-distribution}$$

  where

  $$S^2 = \frac{\sum X^2 - n\bar{X}^2}{n-1}.$$

There are a family of t-distributions and, in a similar way to the chi squared distribution you met in book S3, they are distinguished by the degrees of freedom ν so we usually talk about a t-distribution with ν degrees of freedom' or for short 'the t_ν-distribution'. The test statistic t used here has $n - 1$ degrees of freedom so $\nu = n - 1$.

The t_ν-distribution is symmetrical about zero and, as the single parameter $\nu \to \infty$, $t_\nu \to N(0, 1^2)$. (This is why for large n you could use z as an approximation for t.) For smaller values of ν, the curve is much flatter as can be seen from the diagram.

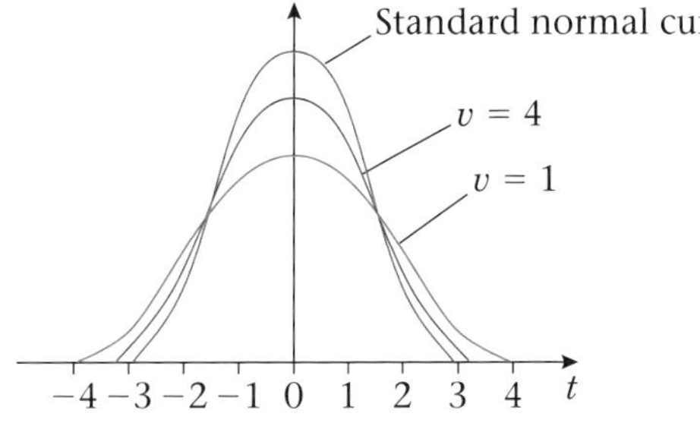

W. S. Gosset, who published his works under the pseudonym 'the student', first investigated the probability distribution of $\frac{(\bar{X} - \mu)}{\frac{S}{\sqrt{n}}}$ when the sample had been taken **from a normal distribution**. The resulting distribution is known as 'student's t-distribution', or more commonly just the t-distribution.

Tables of the *t*-distribution

When dealing with the normal distribution we could have a single table that gave the probability, $\Phi(z)$, of a value being less than or equal to z. To do the same for the student t-distribution would require a table for each value of ν. Since the use of the t-distribution is confined to problems in which you wish to find the value of t which is exceeded with certain probabilities, a table is used that gives values of t that are exceeded with probabilities of 0.1, 0.05, 0.025, 0.01 and 0.005 (10%, 5%, 2.5%, 1% and 0.5%). This is done for a range of different t-distributions, each of which is identified by the value of its parameter ν. You should make yourself familiar with the table (see page 110). A brief extract from the top of the table is shown below.

PERCENTAGE POINTS OF STUDENT'S *t* DISTRIBUTION

The values in the table are those which a random variable with Student's t distribution on ν degrees of freedom exceeds with the probability shown.

ν	0.10	0.05	0.025	0.01	0.005
1	3.078	6.314	12.706	31.821	63.657
2	1.886	2.920	4.303	6.965	9.925
3	1.638	2.353	3.182	4.541	5.841
4	1.533	2.132	2.776	3.747	4.604
5	1.476	2.015	2.571	3.365	4.032
6	1.440	1.943	2.447	3.143	3.707
7	1.415	1.895	2.365	2.998	3.499
8	1.397	1.860	2.306	2.896	3.355

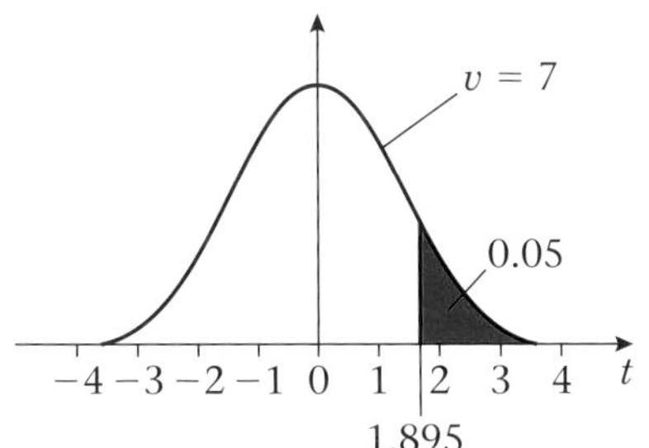

To find, for example, the value of t that is exceeded with a probability of 0.05 if $n = 8$, $\nu = 7$ (the critical value which we shall write as $t_7(0.05)$), you find the intersection of the $\nu = 7$ row and the probability = 0.05 column and read off $t_7(0.05) = 1.895$. The probability that the value of $t < 1.895$ is, of course, $1 - 0.05 = 0.95$ and, by symmetry, the probability that the value of $t < -1.895$ will be 0.05.

Notice that different values of ν ($n - 1$ remember) are down the left-hand column and the probabilities across the top. For values of $\nu > 30$ you may have to go to the nearest value since the table goes up in steps of 2 from 30 to 40, in steps of 5 from 40 to 60 and then in steps of 10 up to 120. For larger values the normal distribution may be used safely.

When working with the t-distributions you are strongly advised to **draw appropriate diagrams** so that you are sure in your own mind which areas under the t-distribution you are dealing with.

Example 1

The random variable X has a t-distribution with 10 degrees of freedom. Determine values of t for which

a $P(X > t) = 0.025$ **b** $P(X < t) = 0.95$

c $P(X < t) = 0.025$ **d** $P(|X| > t) = 0.05$

e $P(|X| < t) = 0.98$

Note $|X|$ means the modulus of X. This is the absolute value of X ignoring the sign. e.g. the modulus of -5, written $|-5|$ is 5. So

$P(|X| > t) = P(X < -t) + P(X > t))$

$P(|X| < t) = P(-t < X < t))$

a  $\nu = 10$

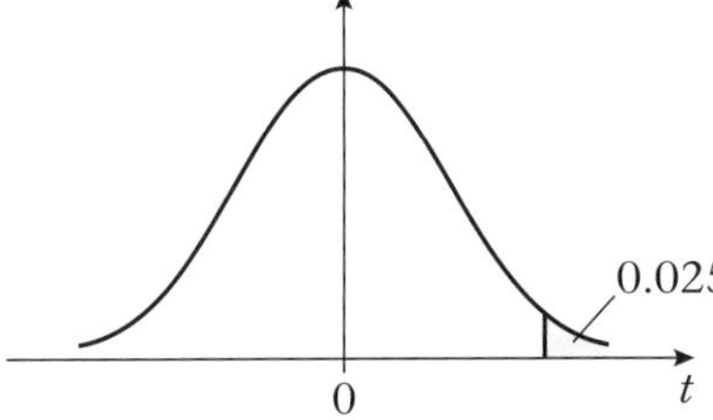

$t_{10}(0.025) = 2.228$

We are looking for $P(X > t)$ so we can use the tables directly. We look where the $\nu = 10$ row intersects with the 0.025 column.

b

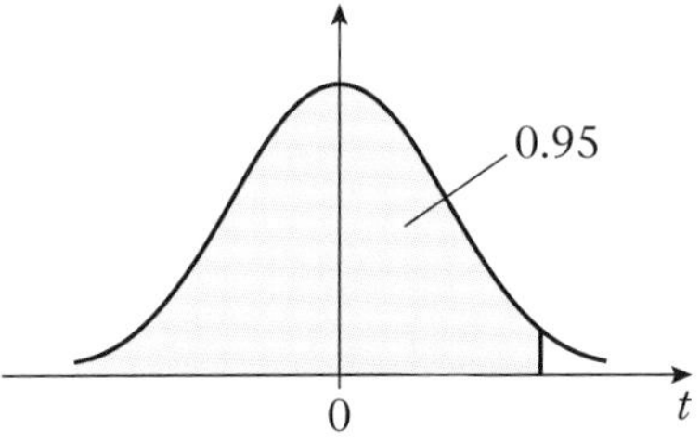

If $P(X < t) = 0.95$ then $P(X > t) = 1 - 0.95 = 0.05$

From the table $t_{10}(0.05) = 1.812$

The whole area under the curve = 1. So $P(X > t) = 1 - P(X < t)$ We look where the $\nu = 10$ row intersects with the 0.05 column.

c

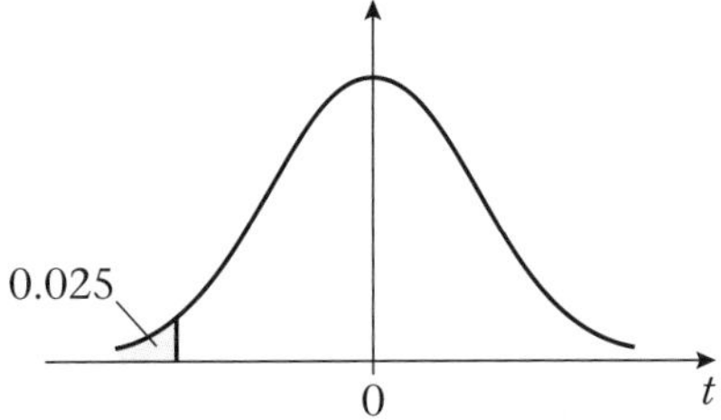

From **a** $P(X > t) = 0.025$ when $t = 2.228$

so $P(X < t) = 0.025$ if $t = -2.228$

Because the distribution is symmetrical $P(X < -t) = P(X > t)$ We know from **a** that $P(X > t) = 0.025$ if $t = 2.228$, so $P(X < t) = 0.025$ when $t = -0.228$

d

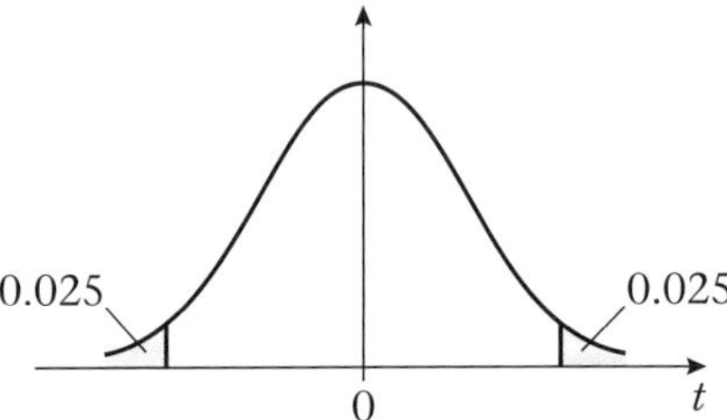

From

a and **c**, $P(|X| > t) = 0.05$ if $X < -2.228$ and $X > 2.228$

There are therefore 2 values for t and they are -2.228 and 2.228

This is two-tailed with probability of 0.025 at each tail.

e

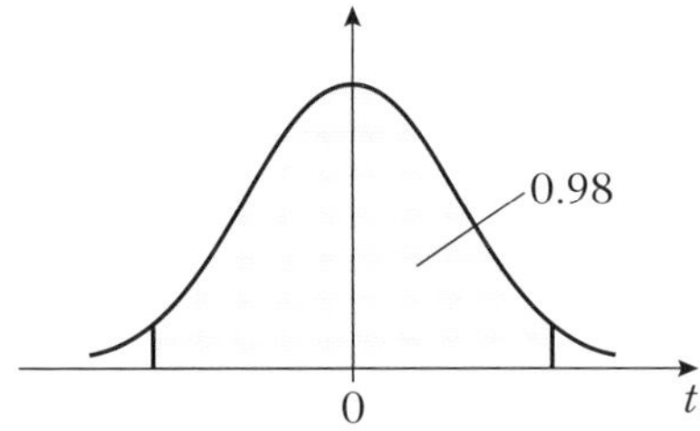

$P(|X| > t) = 0.01$ if $t = 2.764$ and $-2.764 < X < 2.764$

Again there are 2 values of t and they are -2.764 and 2.764

Again, a two-tailed problem. From the diagram you can see that you are looking for tails each with probability 0.01.

Example 2

The random variable Y has a t_4-distribution.
Determine,

a $P(Y > 3.747)$ **b** $P(Y < -2.132)$

a $\nu = 4$

$P(Y > 3.747) = 0.01$

From the $\nu = 4$ row of the table you can see that 3.747 is in the 0.01 probability column.

b $P(Y > 2.132) = 0.05$

By symmetry $P(Y < -2.132) = 0.05$

From the $\nu = 4$ row of the table you can see that 2.132 is in the 0.05 probability column.

Exercise 2A

1 Given that the random variable X has a t_{12}-distibution, find values of t such that,

a $P(X < t) = 0.025$, **b** $P(X > t) = 0.05$, **c** $P(|X| > t) = 0.95$.

2 Given that the random variable X has a t_{26}-distribution. Find

a $t_\nu(0.01)$, **b** $t_\nu(0.05)$.

3 The random variable Y has a t_ν-distribution. Find a value (or values) of t in each of the following.

a $\nu = 10$, $P(Y < t) = 0.95$ **b** $\nu = 32$, $P(Y < t) = 0.005$

c $\nu = 5$, $P(Y < t) = 0.025$ **d** $\nu = 16$, $P(|Y| < t) = 0.98$

e $\nu = 18$, $P(|Y| > t) = 0.10$

2.2 You need to be able to find the confidence interval for the mean of a normal distribution when the variance is unknown.

If a random sample $X_1, X_2, \ldots, X_n$ is selected from $N(\mu, \sigma^2)$ then you can obtain an estimate for the mean μ of the distribution by using $\bar{X}$ as an estimator. You have seen that this is an unbiased estimator, but it would be more helpful if you could give a range of values of μ such that μ will be captured within that range on, for example, 95% of the occasions on which a sample is taken. This is the 95% confidence interval you met in book S3.

If the **variance σ^2 of the population is unknown** then you have seen that

$$t = \frac{(\bar{X} - \mu)}{\frac{S}{\sqrt{n}}} \text{ has a } t_{n-1}\text{-distribution.}$$

Using the table of the t-distribution it is possible, given a value of n, to find a value of t such that

$$P\left(\frac{(\bar{X} - \mu)}{\frac{S}{\sqrt{n}}} > t\right) = 0.025 \text{ and } P\left(\frac{(\bar{X} - \mu)}{\frac{S}{\sqrt{n}}} < -t\right) = 0.025$$

We can call these values the t_{n-1} values for 0.025 probability.

Written $t_{(n-1)}(0.025)$ for short.

$$\text{Thus} \quad P\left(-t_{(n-1)}(0.025) < \frac{(\bar{X} - \mu)}{\frac{S}{\sqrt{n}}} < +t_{(n-1)}(0.025)\right) = 1 - 0.025 - 0.025 = 0.95$$

Look at the inequality inside the bracket.

$$-t_{(n-1)}(0.025) \times \frac{S}{\sqrt{n}} < \bar{X} - \mu < t_{(n-1)}(0.025) \times \frac{S}{\sqrt{n}}$$

$$-t_{(n-1)}(0.025) \times \frac{S}{\sqrt{n}} - \bar{X} < -\mu < t_{(n-1)}(0.025) \times \frac{S}{\sqrt{n}} - \bar{X}$$

$$\bar{X} - t_{(n-1)}(0.025) \times \frac{S}{\sqrt{n}} < \mu < \bar{X} + t_{(n-1)}(0.025) \times \frac{S}{\sqrt{n}}$$

We are interested in μ, so here we try to isolate it by
1 multiplying by $\frac{S}{\sqrt{n}}$,
2 subtracting $\bar{X}$,
3 multiplying by -1 and altering the inequality.

For a particular sample with mean $\bar{x}$, and variance s^2, this becomes:

$$P\left(\bar{x} - t_{(n-1)}(0.025) \times \frac{s}{\sqrt{n}} < \mu < \bar{x} + t_{(n-1)}(0.025) \times \frac{s}{\sqrt{n}}\right) = 0.95$$

The upper and lower values of $\bar{x}$ are again called the 95% confidence limits.

- The 95% confidence limits are given by $\bar{x} \pm t_{(n-1)}(0.025) \times \frac{s}{\sqrt{n}}$
- The 95% confidence interval for the mean of a normal distribution with unknown variance is given by

$$\left(\bar{x} - t_{(n-1)}(0.025) \times \frac{s}{\sqrt{n}}, \quad \bar{x} + t_{(n-1)}(0.025) \times \frac{s}{\sqrt{n}}\right)$$

In the same way

- The 90% confidence limits are given by $\bar{x} \pm t_{(n-1)}(0.05) \times \frac{s}{\sqrt{n}}$
- The 90% confidence interval for the mean of a normal distribution with unknown variance is given by

$$\left(\bar{x} - t_{(n-1)}(0.05) \times \frac{s}{\sqrt{n}}, \quad \bar{x} - t_{(n-1)}(0.05) \times \frac{s}{\sqrt{n}}\right)$$

In general, if the probability of being outside the confidence limits is α,

- **The 100(1 − α)% confidence limits are given by**

$$\bar{x} \pm t_{(n-1)}\frac{\alpha}{2} \times \frac{s}{\sqrt{n}}$$

- **The 100(1 − α)% confidence interval for the mean of a normal distribution with unknown variance is given by**

$$\left(\bar{x} - t_{(n-1)}\frac{\alpha}{2} \times \frac{s}{\sqrt{n}},\ \bar{x} + t_{(n-1)}\frac{\alpha}{2} \times \frac{s}{\sqrt{n}}\right)$$

Example 3

A sample of 6 trout taken from a fish farm were caught and their lengths in centimetres were measured. The lengths of the fish were as follows:

26.8 26.0 25.8 25.5 24.3 24.6

Assuming that the lengths of trout are normally distributed, find a 90% confidence interval for the mean length of trout in the fish farm.

Using a calculator gives $\bar{x} = 25.5$ and $s^2 = 0.8560$

$s = \sqrt{0.8560} = 0.9252$

First find the sample mean and variance.

The standard deviation of the sample can be found by taking the square root of the variance.

The 90% confidence limits for $\bar{x}$ are

$$\bar{x} \pm t_5(5\%)\frac{s}{\sqrt{n}} = 25.5 \pm 2.015 \times \frac{0.9252}{\sqrt{6}}$$
$$= 25.5 \pm 0.761$$

The 90% confidence interval is (24.739, 26.261)

Put your values for $\bar{x}$ and s into the formula, and work out the confidence interval.

Example 4

The percentage starch content of potatoes is normally distributed with mean μ. In order to assess the mean value of the starch content a random sample of twelve potatoes is selected and their starch content measured. The percentages of starch contents obtained were as follows:

23.2 20.3 18.6 20.0 20.8 21.6 19.4 18.7 22.1 19.5 21.3 22.6

Find a 95% confidence interval for the mean.

$\bar{x} = 20.675$ and $s = 1.513$ — You could use a calculator to find these.

The 95% confidence limits for $\bar{x}$ are

$$\bar{x} + t_{11}(2.5\%)\frac{s}{\sqrt{n}} = 20.675 \pm 2.201 \times \frac{1.513}{\sqrt{12}}$$ — Use the formula.

$$= 20.675 \pm 0.961$$

The 95% confidence interval is (19.714, 21.636) — Write out the confidence interval.

Exercise 2B

1 A test on the life (in hours) of a certain make of torch batteries gave the following results:

20.3   17.3   25.0   18.4   16.3   24.8   24.3   21.2

Assuming that the lifetime of batteries is normally distributed, find a 90% confidence interval for the mean.

2 A sample of size 16 taken from a normal population with unknown variance gave the following sample values $\bar{x} = 12.4$, $s^2 = 21.0$. Find a 95% confidence interval on the population mean.

3 The mean heights (measured in centimetres) of six male students at a college were as follows:

182   178   183   180   169   184

Calculate,

a a 90% confidence interval and

b a 95% confidence interval for the mean height of male students at the college.
You may assume that the heights are normally distributed.

4 The masses (in grams) of 10 nails selected at random from a bin of 90 cm long nails were:

9.7   10.2   11.2   9.4   11.0   11.2   9.8   9.8   10.0   11.3

Calculate a 98% confidence interval for the mean mass of the nails, assuming that their mass is normally distributed.

5 It is known that the length of men's feet is normally distributed. A random sample of the feet of 8 adult males gave the following summary statistics of length x (in cm):

$\sum x = 224.1$ $\sum x^2 = 6337.39$

Calculate a 99% confidence interval for the mean lengths of men's feet based upon these results.

6 A random sample of 26 students from the sixth form of a school sat an intelligence test that measured their IQs. The result are summarised below

$\bar{x} = 122$ $s^2 = 225$

Assuming that the IQ is normally distributed, calculate a 95% confidence interval for the mean IQ of the students.

2.3 You need to be able to carry out hypothesis testing for the mean of a normal distribution with unknown variance.

Apart from using the t-distribution rather than the normal distribution for finding the critical region, testing the mean of a normal distribution with unknown variance follows the same steps as you used when testing the mean of a normal distribution with known variance.

The following steps might help you in answering questions about hypothesis testing of the mean of a normal distribution with unknown variance.

1 Write down H_0.

2 Write down H_1.

3 Specify the significance level α.

4 Write down the number of degrees of freedom ν.

5 Write down the critical region.

6 Calculate $\bar{x}$, s^2 and t using

$$\bar{x} = \frac{\sum x}{n},\ s^2 = \frac{1}{n-1}\left[\sum x^2 - \frac{(\sum x)^2}{n}\right] \quad \left(\text{or } s^2 = \frac{\sum x^2 - n\bar{x}^2}{n-1}\right) \text{ and } t = \frac{\bar{x} - \mu}{\frac{s}{\sqrt{n}}}$$

7 Conclusions

The following points should be addressed:

i is the result significant or not?

ii what are the implications in terms of the original problem?

Example 5

A shopkeeper sells jars of jam. The weights of the jars of jam are normally distributed with a mean of 150 g. A customer complains that the mean weight of 8 jars she had bought was only 147 g. An estimate for the standard deviation of the weights of the 8 jars of jam calculated from the 8 observations was 2 g.

a Test at the 5% significance level whether 147 g is significantly less than the quoted mean.

b Discuss whether the customer has cause for complaint.

a $H_0: \mu = 150 \qquad H_1: \mu < 150$

Significance level = 0.05 (one-tail test).

$\nu = 8 - 1 = 7$

From tables the critical value t_7 is -1.895

so the critical region is $t \leqslant -1.895$

$\bar{x} = 147$, $\mu = 150$, $s = 2$

$$t = \frac{\bar{x} - \mu}{\frac{s}{\sqrt{n}}} = \frac{147 - 150}{\frac{2}{\sqrt{8}}} = -4.2426$$

Now $-4.2426 < -1.895$ so the result is significant and H_0 is rejected.

b There is evidence to suggest that the mean weight is less than 150 g and the customer does have a cause for complaint.

1 State your hypotheses (we are interested to see if jars are underweight so < for H_1).

2 Write down the significance level.

3 Find the number of degrees of freedom ($n - 1$ in this case).

4 Look up the critical value in the table and note a minus sign is needed since a left-hand tail is being used.

5 Write down the critical region.

6 Calculate $\bar{x}$, μ and s
Use these to calculate t.

7 Draw a conclusion.
Put it in the context of the original problem.

Example 6

The temperatures (°C) were measured at noon on 10 days during the month of March in West Cumbria. The readings were:

12.8 11.4 12.9 15.1 15.4 13.5 14.9 15.0 16.0 15.8

Using a 5% significance level, test whether or not this is an increase over the previous year when the average noon day temperature was 13.5°C.

$H_0: \mu = 13.5 \qquad H_1: \mu > 13.5$

1 State your hypotheses (we are interested to see if there is an increase so $>$ for H_1).

Significance level 5%

2 Write down the significance level.

$\nu = 9$

3 Find the number of degrees of freedom ($n - 1$ in this case).

From table the critical value is $t_9 = 1.833$

4 Look up the critical value in the table and

so the critical region is $t \geqslant 1.833$

5 write down the critical region.

$$\bar{x} = \frac{12.8 + 11.4 + 12.9 + 15.1 + 15.4 + 13.5 + 14.9 + 15.0 + 16.0 + 15.8}{10}$$

$= 14.28$

6 Calculate $\bar{x}$

$$s^2 = \frac{\sum x^2 - n\bar{x}^2}{n-1} = \frac{2060.28 - 10 \times (14.28)^2}{10 - 1} = 2.344$$

and

$s = 1.531$

s

Note both of these are easily found using a calculator.

$$t = \frac{\bar{x} - \mu}{\frac{s}{\sqrt{n}}} = \frac{14.28 - 13.5}{\frac{1.531}{\sqrt{10}}} = 1.611$$

Calculate t.

$1.611 < 1.833$ so the result is not critical.

There is no evidence to suggest that the average temperature has increased.

7 Draw a conclusion.

Example 7

A concrete manufacturer tests cubes of its concrete at regular intervals, and their compressive strengths in $\mathrm{N\,m^{-1}}$ are determined. The mean value of the strengths is required to be $0.47\,\mathrm{N\,m^{-1}}$. A new supplier of cement offers to supply the firm at a cheaper rate than the present supplier, and a trial bag of cement is used to make 12 concrete cubes. Upon testing, these cubes are found to have strengths (x) such that $\sum x = 5.52$ and $\sum x^2 = 2.542$. Assume that the strengths are normally distributed.

a Stating your hypotheses clearly test, at the 5% level of significance, whether or not the use of the new cement has altered the mean strength of the concrete.

In the light of your conclusion to the test in part **a**,

b what would you recommend the manufacturer to do?

a $H_0: \mu = 0.47 \qquad H_1: \mu \neq 0.47$

$\nu = 12 - 1 = 11$

From tables the critical value is 2.201

The critical region is $|t| \geqslant 2.201$

$$\bar{x} = \frac{\sum x}{n} = \frac{5.52}{12} = 0.46\,\text{N m}^{-1},$$

$$s^2 = \frac{\sum x^2 - n\bar{x}^2}{n-1} = \frac{2.542 - 12 \times 0.46^2}{11} = 0.0002545$$

$s = 0.016$

$$t = \frac{\bar{x} - \mu}{\frac{s}{\sqrt{n}}} = \frac{0.46 - 0.47}{\frac{0.016}{\sqrt{12}}} = -2.165$$

Now $|-2.165| < |-2.201|$

The result is not critical. There is not enough evidence to suggest that the mean strength has altered.

b It seems that, since the mean strength has not altered, the manufacturer should accept the new supplier because he is cheaper. The two values −2.165 and −2.201 are quite close, however, and a one-tailed test of whether or not the strength had decreased should be done, or failing this a further sample could be taken.

We are looking to see if the strength has altered up or down so we use $\neq$ in H_1.

Remember to use a 0.025 significance level since it is a two-tailed test.

Since we are given $\sum x$ and $\sum x^2$ in the question we use these formulae.

Since $\bar{x} < \mu$, t is negative.

t lies between −2.201 and +2.201

Draw the conclusion in context.

Base your recommendation on the conclusion you drew.

Exercise 2C

1 Given that the observations 9, 11, 11, 12, 14, have been drawn from a normal distribution, test $H_0: \mu = 11$ against $H_1: \mu > 11$. Use a 5% significance level.

2 A random sample of size 28 taken from a normally distributed variable gave the following sample values $\bar{x} = 17.1$ and $s^2 = 4$. Test $H_0: \mu = 19$ against $H_1: \mu < 19$. Use a 1% level of significance.

3 A random sample of size 13 taken from a normally distributed variable gave the following sample values $\bar{x} = 3.26$, $s^2 = 0.64$. Test $H_0: \mu = 3$ against $H_1: \mu \neq 3$. Use a 5% significance level.

4 A certain brand of blanched hazelnuts for use in cooking is sold in packets. The weights of the packets of hazelnuts follow a normal distribution with mean μ. The manufacturer claims that $\mu = 100$ g. A sample of 15 packets was taken and the weight x of each was measured. The results are summarised by the following statistics $\sum x = 1473$, $\sum x^2 = 148\,119$.

Test at the 5% significance level whether or not there is evidence to justify the manufacturer's claim.

5 A manufacturer claims that the lifetimes of its 100 watt bulbs are normally distributed with a mean of 1000 hours. A laboratory tests 8 bulbs and finds their lifetimes to be 985, 920, 1110, 1040, 945, 1165, 1170, and 1055 hours.

Stating your hypotheses clearly, examine whether or not the bulbs have a longer mean life than that claimed. Use a 5% level of significance.

6 A fertiliser manufacturer claims that by using brand F fertiliser the yield of fruit bushes will be increased. A random sample of 14 fruit bushes was fertilised with brand F and the resulting yields, x, were summarised by $\sum x = 90.8$, $\sum x^2 = 600$. The yield of bushes fertilised by the usual fertiliser was normally distributed with a mean of 6 kg per bush.

Test, at the 2.5% significance level, the manufacturer's claim.

7 A nuclear reprocessing company claims that the amount of radiation within a reprocessing building in which there had been an accident had been reduced to an acceptable level by their clean up team. The amount of radiation, x, at 20 sites within the building in suitable units are summarised by $\sum x = 21.7$, $\sum x^2 = 28.4$. Before the accident the level of radiation in the building was normally distributed with a mean of 1.00. Test, at the 0.10 level whether or not the claim is justified.

2.4 You need to be able to find the distribution of the variance of a sample taken from a normal distribution.

If you take a sample of n independent observations $X_1, X_2, \ldots, X_n$ with sample mean $\bar{X}$ then $S^2 = \frac{1}{n-1}\sum(X_i - \bar{X})^2$ is an unbiased estimator of σ^2.

Different samples from the same population will give different estimates for μ and σ^2, so in the same way that $\bar{x}$ is a particular value of the random variable $\bar{X}$, s^2 is a particular value of a random variable S^2.

The distribution of S^2 is not easy to find, and is beyond the scope of this book, but the distribution of $\frac{(n-1)S^2}{\sigma^2}$ is known, and is a distribution that you met in book S3, namely the chi-squared distribution with $n - 1$ degrees of freedom.

- **If a random sample of n observations $X_1. X_2, \ldots, X_n$ is selected from $N(\mu, \sigma^2)$ then**

$$\frac{(n-1)S^2}{\sigma^2} \sim \chi^2_{(n-1)}$$

Percentage points of the chi-squared distribution

Percentage points for the χ^2_{n-1} distribution are given in the table on page 106. The number of degrees of freedom $\nu = n - 1$ are given down the left hand side of the table and the percentages along the top. To read the value of χ^2_ν which is exceeded with probability p, you find the intersection of the p column with the ν row.

ν	0.995	0.990	0.975	0.950	0.900	0.100	0.050	0.025	0.010	0.005
1	0.000	0.000	0.001	0.004	0.016	2.705	3.841	5.024	6.635	7.879
2	0.010	0.020	0.051	0.103	0.211	4.605	5.991	7.378	9.210	10.597
3	0.072	0.115	0.216	0.352	0.584	6.251	7.815	9.348	11.345	12.838
4	0.207	0.296	0.484	0.711	1.064	7.779	9.488	11.143	13.277	14.860
5	0.412	0.554	0.831	1.145	1.610	9.236	11.070	12.832	15.086	16.750
6	0.676	0.872	1.237	1.635	2.204	10.645	12.592	14.449	16.812	18.548
7	0.989	1.239	1.690	2.167	2.833	12.017	14.067	16.013	18.475	20.278

For example $\chi_6^2\,(0.95) = 1.635$ so the probability of χ_6^2 exceeding 1.635 is 95%. You should note that the probability that χ_6^2 is less than 1.635 is $100 - 95 = 5\%$.

For example if you wish to find $\chi_4^2\,(0.05)$ you look down the 0.05 column until you met the row $\nu = 4$, and read off 9.488

Because the χ^2 distribution is non-symmetric **both tails of the distribution are given in the table**.

2.5 You need to be able to find the confidence interval for the variance of a normal distribution.

If a random sample $X_1, X_2, \ldots, X_n$ is taken from a $N(\mu, \sigma)$ distribution then $\frac{(n-1)S^2}{\sigma^2}$ has a χ^2_{n-1} distribution. Using the table of percentage points of the distribution χ^2_{n-1} you can find given values of $\frac{(n-1)S^2}{\sigma^2}$ such that σ^2 will be captured within the interval between them on 95% of such occasions. Thus, assuming that the two tails are of equal size,

$$\chi^2_{n-1}(0.975) < \frac{(n-1)S^2}{\sigma^2} < \chi^2_{n-1}(0.025)$$

$$\frac{1}{\chi^2_{n-1}(0.025)} < \frac{\sigma^2}{(n-1)S^2} < \frac{1}{\chi^2_{n-1}(0.975)}$$

$$\frac{(n-1)S^2}{\chi^2_{n-1}(0.025)} < \sigma^2 < \frac{(n-1)S^2}{\chi^2_{n-1}(0.975)}$$

We want to get bounds for σ^2 so we isolate it by

1 turning the fractions upside down and reversing the inequality,

2 multiplying by $(n-1)S^2$

If you have a specific estimate s^2 this becomes

$$\frac{(n-1)s^2}{\chi^2_{n-1}(0.975)} < \sigma^2 < \frac{(n-1)s^2}{\chi^2_{n-1}(0.025)}$$

The values $\frac{(n-1)s^2}{\chi^2_{n-1}(0.025)}$ and $\frac{(n-1)s^2}{\chi^2_{n-1}(0.975)}$ are known as the lower and upper 95% confidence limits respectively, and the interval in-between is called the 95% confidence interval.

- The 95% confidence limits are $\frac{(n-1)s^2}{\chi^2_{n-1}(0.025)}$ and $\frac{(n-1)s^2}{\chi^2_{n-1}(0.975)}$

- The 95% confidence interval for the variance of a normal distribution is $\left(\frac{(n-1)s^2}{\chi^2_{n-1}(0.025)}, \frac{(n-1)s^2}{\chi^2_{n-1}(0.975)}\right)$

In a similar way

The 90% confidence limits are $\frac{(n-1)s^2}{\chi^2_{n-1}(0.05)}$ and $\frac{(n-1)s^2}{\chi^2_{n-1}(0.95)}$

The 90% confidence interval for the variance of a normal distribution is $\left(\frac{(n-1)s^2}{\chi^2_{n-1}(0.05)}, \frac{(n-1)s^2}{\chi^2_{n-1}(0.95)}\right)$

Generally, for a probability of α that the variance falls outside the limits,

- **The 100(1 − α)% confidence limits are**
$$\frac{(n-1)s^2}{\chi^2_{n-1}\left(\frac{\alpha}{2}\right)} \text{ and } \frac{(n-1)s^2}{\chi^2_{n-1}\left(1-\frac{\alpha}{2}\right)}$$

- **The 100(1 − α)% confidence interval for the variance of a normal distribution is**
$$\left(\frac{(n-1)s^2}{\chi^2_{n-1}\left(\frac{\alpha}{2}\right)}, \frac{(n-1)s^2}{\chi^2_{n-1}\left(1-\frac{\alpha}{2}\right)}\right)$$

Example 8

In order to discover the accuracy of a new rifle 8 marksmen were selected at random to fire the rifle at a target. The distances x, in mm, of the 8 shots from the centre of the target were as follows:

10, 14, 12, 8, 6, 11, 18, 14

Assuming that the distances are normally distributed, find 95% confidence limits for the variance.

$\bar{x} = 11.625$ $s^2 = 14.2679$

You can use a calculator to find $\bar{x}$ and s^2.

$\chi^2_7(0.975) = 1.690.$ $\chi^2_7(0.025) = 16.013$

Then find the percentage points of χ^2_7 from the table.

$$\frac{(n-1)s^2}{\chi^2_{n-1}(0.025)} = \frac{7 \times 14.2679}{16.013} = 6.2371$$

$$\frac{(n-1)s^2}{\chi^2_{n-1}(0.975)} = \frac{7 \times 14.2679}{1.690} = 59.0976$$

Now find the critical points for the variance.

The 95% confidence interval for the variance is (6.237, 59.098).

Don't forget to write out the interval.

Example 9

A company manufactures 12 amp electrical fuses.
A random sample of 10 fuses was taken from a batch and the failure current (X) measured for each. The results are summarised below:

$\sum x = 118.9$ $\sum x^2 = 1414.89$

Assume that the data can be regarded as a random sample from a normal population.

a Calculate an unbiased estimate for the variance of the batch based upon the sample.

b Use your estimate from **a** to calculate a 95% confidence interval for

  i the mean,

  ii the standard deviation.

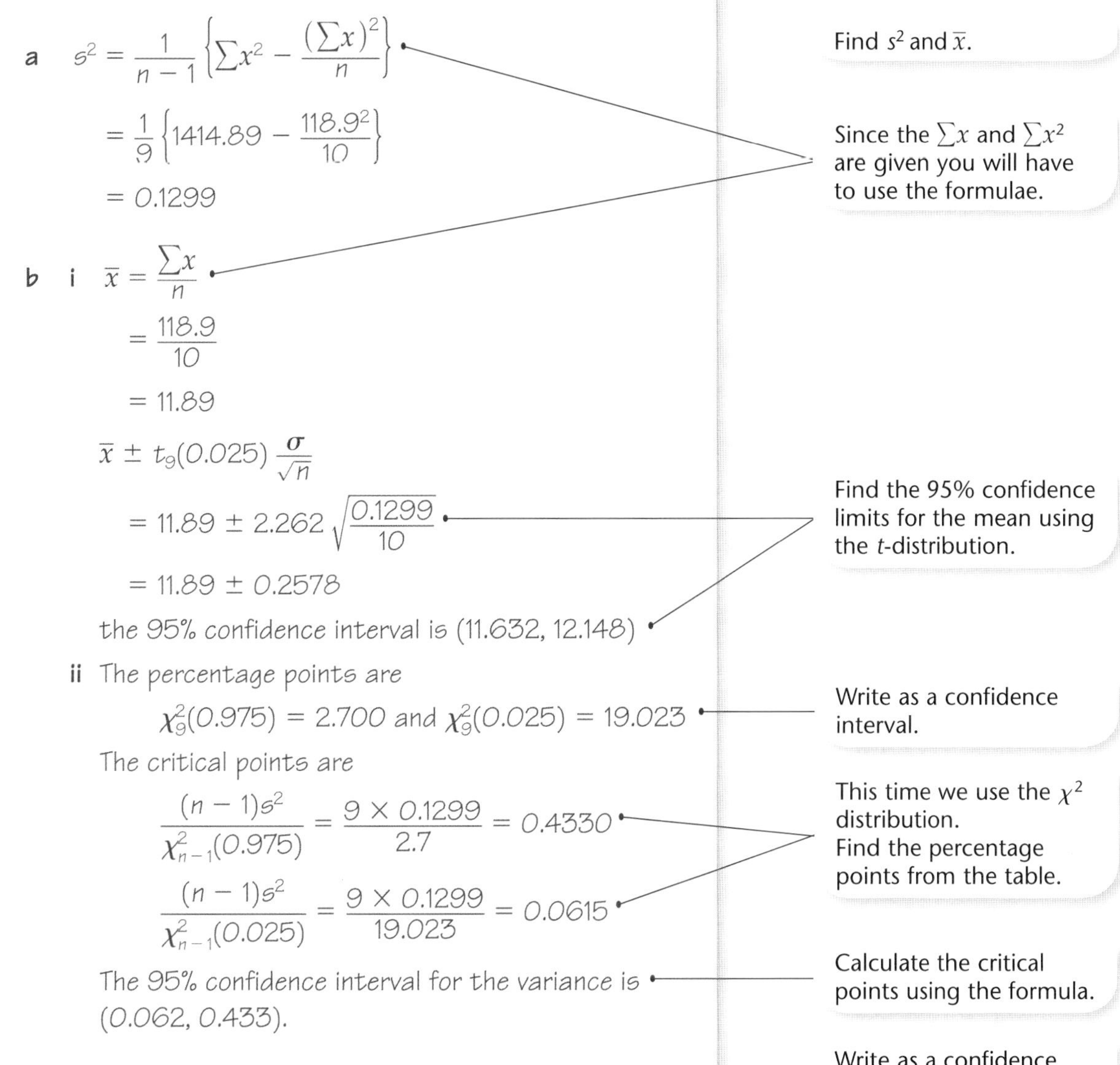

Exercise 2D

1 A random sample of 15 observations of a normal population gave an unbiased estimate for the variance of the population of $s^2 = 4.8$. Calculate a 95% confidence interval for the population variance.

2 A random sample of 20 observations of a normally distributed variable X is summarised by $\sum x = 132.4$ and $\sum x^2 = 884.3$. Calculate a 90% confidence interval for the variance of X.

3 A random sample of 14 observations is taken from a population that is assumed to be normally distributed. The resulting values were:

2.3, 3.9, 3.5, 2.2, 2.6, 2.5, 2.3, 3.9, 2.1, 3.6, 2.1, 2.7, 3.2, 3.4

Calculate a 95% confidence interval for the population variance.

4 A random sample of female voles was trapped in a wood. Their lengths, in centimetres (excluding tails) were 7.5, 8.4, 10.1, 6.2, and 8.4 cm.

Assuming that this is a sample from a normal distribution, calculate 95% confidence intervals for:

a the mean length,

b the variance of the lengths of female voles.

5 **a** A random sample of 10 is taken from the annual rainfall figures, x cm, in a certain district. The result is summarised by $\sum x = 621$ and $\sum x^2 = 38\,938$

Calculate 90% confidence limits for,

i the mean annual rainfall,

ii the variance of the annual rainfall.

b What assumption have you made about the distribution of the annual rainfall in part **a**?

6 A new variety of small daffodil is grown in the trial ground of a nursery. During the flowering period a random sample of 10 flowers was taken and the lengths, in millimetres, of their stalks were measured. The results were as follows:

266, 254, 215, 220, 253, 230, 216, 248, 234, 244

Assuming that the lengths are normally distributed, calculate 95% confidence intervals for the mean and variance of the lengths.

2.6 You need to be able to carry out a hypothesis test for the variance of a normal distribution.

Suppose that a manufacturer of pistons for cars had a machine that finished the diameter of the piston to size. The machine was set up so that it produced the pistons with a diameter that was normally distributed with mean 60 mm and standard deviation 0.03 mm. After the machine had been running for some time a sample of 15 pistons was taken and the mean of the size of the pistons in the sample was still 60 mm but the best estimate of the variance calculated from the sample was 0.002 mm². The question the manufacturer wishes to have answered is 'has the variance increased?'

As usual with such questions a significance level has to be set so let us imagine that it is 5%.

Putting the manufacturer's question in the form of hypotheses you get:

$H_0: \sigma^2 = 0.03^2$ $\qquad$ $H_1: \sigma^2 > 0.03^2$

If H_0 is assumed true then $\frac{(n-1)S^2}{\sigma^2}$ will be a single observation from a χ^2 distribution.

Since in this case $s^2 > \sigma^2$ then, as in previous hypothesis tests, you would have to ask 'could you get the calculated value of $\frac{(n-1)S^2}{\sigma^2}$ if H_0 were true?' The critical value separating the acceptance and rejection regions will be the relevant percentage point of the χ^2_{n-1} distribution.

In this case $\nu = n - 1 = 15 - 1 = 14$, and the percentage is 0.05.

From the table $\chi^2_{14}(0.05) = 23.685$, and the critical region is $\frac{(n-1)s^2}{\sigma^2} \geqslant 23.685$

The value of the test statistic will be $\frac{(n-1)s^2}{\sigma^2}$.

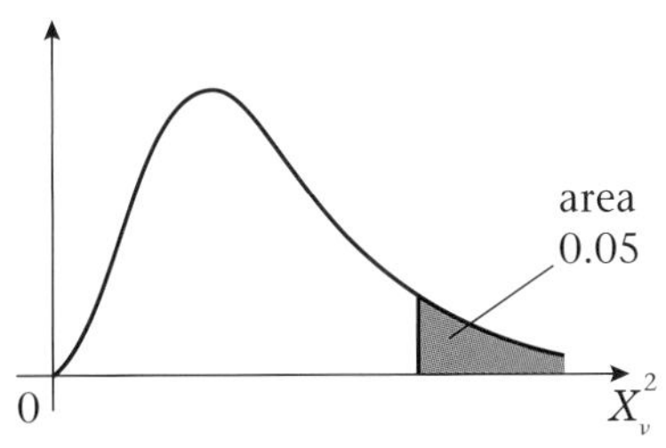

In the manufacturer's case $\frac{(n-1)s^2}{\sigma^2} = \frac{(15-1)0.002}{0.03^2} = 31.11$

31.11 is in the critical region so the result is significant and H_0 is rejected. The variance has increased.

Note that again there are 7 steps to be followed.

1 Write down the null hypothesis (H_0).

2 Write down the alternative hypotheses (H_1).

3 Specify α.

4 Write down the degrees of freedom ν.

5 Write down the critical region.

6 Identify the population variance σ^2 and the unbiased estimate s^2 and calculate the value of the test statistic $\frac{(n-1)s^2}{\sigma^2}$

7 Complete your test and state your conclusions. The following points should be addressed:
 i is the result significant?
 ii what are the implications in the context of the original problem?

Example 10

A random sample of 12 observations is taken from a normal distribution with a variance of σ^2. The unbiased estimate of the population variance is calculated as 0.015

a Test at the 5% level, the hypothesis that $\sigma^2 = 0.025$ against the alternative hypothesis that $\sigma^2 \neq 0.025$

b What conclusion can you draw from the test in part **a**?

a $H_0: \sigma^2 = 0.025$ $H_1: \sigma^2 \neq 0.025$.

1 and **2** Write down the hypotheses.

Significance level 5% (2.5% at each tail)

3 Write down the significance level.

$\nu = 11$

4 Write down the degrees of freedom ($n - 1$).

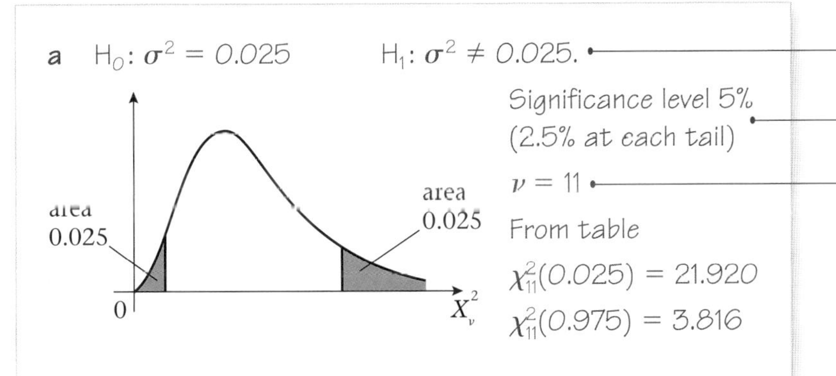

From table

$\chi^2_{11}(0.025) = 21.920$

$\chi^2_{11}(0.975) = 3.816$

This test is 2-tailed so there will be 2 critical values.

5 Find the critical values and the critical region.

The critical region is $\frac{(n-1)s^2}{\sigma^2} \geqslant 21.920$ and $\frac{(n-1)s^2}{\sigma^2} \leqslant 3.816$

$\sigma^2 = 0.025 \qquad s^2 = 0.015$

Test statistic $\frac{(n-1)s^2}{\sigma^2} = \frac{(12-1)0.015}{0.025} = 6.6$

6 Calculate the test statistic.

$3.816 < 6.6 < 21.920$

6.6 is not in the critical region so there is insufficient evidence for rejecting H_0.

7 Draw a conclusion.

b There has been no change in the variance.

Put your conclusion in context.

Exercise 2E

1 Twenty random observations (x) are taken from a normal distribution with variance σ^2. The results are summarised as follows:

$$\sum x = 332.1, \sum x^2 = 5583.63$$

a Calculate an unbiased estimate for the population variance.

b Test, at the 5% significance level, the hypothesis $H_0: \sigma^2 = 1.5$ against the hypothesis $H_1: \sigma^2 > 1.5$

2 A random sample of 10 observations is taken from a normal distribution with variance σ^2 which is thought to be equal to 0.09. The results were as follows:

0.35, 0.42, 0.30, 0.26, 0.31, 0.30, 0.40, 0.33, 0.30, 0.40

Test, at the 0.025% level of significance, the hypothesis $H_0: \sigma^2 = 0.09$ against the hypothesis $H_1: \sigma^2 < 0.09$

3 The following random observations are taken from a normal distribution which is thought to have a variance of 4.1:

2.1, 2.3, 3.5, 4.6, 5.0, 6.4, 7.1, 8.6, 8.7, 9.1

Test, at the 5% significance level, the hypothesis $H_0: \sigma^2 = 4.1$ against the hypothesis $H_1: \sigma^2 \neq 4.1$

4 It is claimed that the masses of a particular component produced in a small factory are normally distributed and have a mean mass of 10 g and a standard deviation of 1.12 g.

A random sample of 20 such components was found to have a variance of 1.15 g.

Test, at the 5% significance level, the hypothesis $H_0: \sigma^2 = 1.12^2$ against the hypothesis $H_1: \sigma^2 \neq 1.12^2$

5 Rollers for use in roller bearings are produced on a certain machine. The rollers are supposed be normally distributed and to have a mean diameter (μ) of 10 mm with a variance (σ^2) of 0.04 mm^2.

A random sample of 15 rollers from the machine have their diameters, x in millimetres, measured. The results are summarised below:

$$\sum x = 149.941 \qquad \sum x^2 = 1498.83$$

a Calculate unbiased estimates for μ and σ^2.

b Test at the 5% significance level,

i the hypothesis $\mu = 10$ against the hypothesis $\mu \neq 10$, using your estimate for σ^2 as the true variance of the population

ii the hypothesis $\sigma^2 = 0.04$ against the hypothesis $\sigma^2 \neq 0.04$

6 The diameters of the eggs of the little gull are approximately normally distributed with mean 4.11 cm with a variance of 0.19 cm^2.

A sample of 8 little gulls eggs from a particular island which were measured had diameters in centimetres as follows:

4.4, 4.5, 4.1, 3.9, 4.4, 4.6, 4.5, 4.1

a Calculate an unbiased estimate for the variance of the population of little gull eggs on the island.

b Calculate an unbiased estimate of the mean diameter of the eggs and, test, at the 5% level, the hypothesis $\mu = 4.11$ against the hypothesis $\mu > 4.11$

c Test, at the 10% significance level, the hypothesis $\sigma^2 = 0.19$ against the hypothesis $\sigma^2 \neq 0.19$

7 Climbing rope produced by a certain manufacturer is known to have a mean tensile breaking strength (μ) of 170.2 kg and standard deviation 10.5 kg. The breaking strength of the rope is normally distributed.

A new component is added to the material which will, it is claimed, decrease the standard deviation without altering the tensile strength. A random sample of 20 pieces of the new rope is selected and each is tested to destruction. The tensile strength of each piece is noted. The results are used to calculate unbiased estimates of the mean strength and standard deviation of the population of new rope. These were found to be 172.4 kg and 8.5 kg.

a Test at the 5% level whether or not the variance has been reduced.

b What recommendation would you make to the manufacturer?

Mixed exercise 2F

1 A random sample of 14 observations is taken from a normal distribution. The sample has a mean $\bar{x} = 30.4$ and a sample variance $s^2 = 36$

It is suggested that the population mean is 28. Test this hypothesis at the 5% level of significance.

2 A random sample of 8 observations is taken from a random variable X that is normally distributed. The sample gave the following summary statistics

$$\sum x^2 = 970.25 \qquad \sum x = 85$$

The population mean is thought to be 10. Test this hypothesis against the alternative hypothesis that the mean is greater than 10. Use the 5% level of significance.

3 Six eggs selected at random from the daily output of a battery of hens had the following weights in grams.

55, 50, 53, 53, 52, 54

Calculate 95% confidence intervals for

a the mean,

b the variance of the population from which these eggs were taken.

c What assumption have you made about the distribution of the weights of eggs?

4 A sample of size 18 was taken from a random variable X which was normally distributed, producing the following summary statistics.

$\bar{x} = 9.8$ $\quad s^2 = 0.49$

Calculate 95% confidence intervals for

a the mean,

b the variance of the population.

5 A random sample of 14 observations was taken of a random variable X which was normally distributed. The sample had a mean $\bar{x} = 23.8$, and a variance $s^2 = 1.8$

Calculate,

a a 95% confidence interval for the variance of the population,

b a 90% confidence interval for the variance of the population.

6 A manufacturer claims that the lifetime of its batteries is normally distributed with mean 21.5 hours. A laboratory tests 8 batteries and finds the lifetimes of these batteries to be as follows:

19.7 18.4 22.2 20.8 16.9 25.3 23.2 21.1

Stating clearly your hypotheses, examine whether or not these lifetimes indicate that the batteries have a shorter mean lifetime than that claimed by the company. Use a 5% level of significance. **E**

7 A diabetic patient monitors his blood glucose in mmol/l at random times of the day over several days. The following is a random sample of the results for this patient.

5.1 5.8 6.1 6.8 6.2 5.1 6.3 6.6 6.1 7.9 5.8 6.5

Assuming the data to be normally distributed, calculate a 95% confidence interval for

a the mean of the population of blood glucose readings,

b the standard deviation of the population of blood glucose readings.

The level of blood glucose varies throughout the day according to the consumption of food and the amount of exercise taken during the day.

c Comment on the suitability of the patient's method of data collection. **E**

8 A woollen mill produces scarves. The mill has several machines each operated by a different person. Jane has recently started working at the mill and the supervisor wishes to check the lengths of the scarves Jane is producing. A random sample of 20 scarves is taken and the length, x cm, of each scarf is recorded. The results are summarised as:

$$\sum x = 1428, \qquad \sum x^2 = 102\,286$$

Assuming that the lengths of scarves produced by any individual follow a normal distribution,

a calculate a 95% confidence interval for the variance σ^2 of the lengths of scarves produced by Jane.

The mill's owners require that 90% of scarves should be within 10 cm of the mean length.

b Find the value of σ that would satisfy this condition.

c Explain whether or not the supervisor should be concerned about the scarves Jane is producing. **E**

9 In order to discover the possible error in using a stop-watch, a student started the watch and stopped it again as quickly as she could. The times taken in centiseconds for 6 such attempts are recorded below:

10, 13, 14, 10, 13, 9

Assuming that the times are normally distributed, find 95% confidence limits for

a the mean,

b the variance. **E**

10 A manufacturer claims that the car batteries which it produces have a mean lifetime of 24 months, with a standard deviation of 4 months. A garage selling the batteries doubts this claim and suggests that both values are in fact higher.

The garage monitors the lifetimes of 10 randomly selected batteries and finds that they have a mean lifetime of 27.2 months and a standard deviation of 5.2 months.

Stating clearly your hypotheses and using a 5% level of significance, test the claim made by the manufacturer for

a the standard deviation,

b the mean,

c State an assumption which has to be made when carrying out these tests. **E**

11 The distance to 'take-off' from a standing start of an aircraft was measured on twenty occasions. The results are summarised in the following table.

Distance (m)	Frequency
700–	3
710–	5
720–	9
730–	2
740–750	1

Assuming that distance to 'take-off' is normally distributed, find 95% confidence intervals for

a the mean,

b the standard deviation.

It has been hypothesised that the mean distance to 'take-off' is 725 m.

c Comment on this hypothesis in the light of your interval from part **a**. 

12 The maximum weight that 50 cm lengths of a certain make of string can hold before breaking (the breaking strain) has a normal distribution with mean 40 kg and standard deviation 5 kg. The manufacturer of the string has developed a new process which should increase the mean breaking strain of the string but should not alter the standard deviation. Ten randomly selected pieces of string are tested and their breaking strains, in kg, are:

51, 48, 37, 46, 36, 53, 34, 49, 47, 50

a Stating your hypotheses clearly test, at the 5% level of significance, whether or not the new process has altered the variance.

In the light of your conclusion to the test in part **a**,

b test whether or not there is evidence that the new process has increased the mean breaking strain. State your hypotheses clearly and use a 5% level of significance.

c Explain briefly your choice of test in part **b**. 

13 A company knows from previous experience that the time taken by maintenance engineers to repair a particular electrical fault on a complex piece of electrical equipment is 3.5 hours on average with a standard deviation of 0.5 hours.

A new method of repair has been devised, but before converting to this new method the company took a random sample of 10 of its engineers and each engineer carried out a repair using the new method. The time, x hours, it took each of them to carry out the repair was recorded and the data are summarised below:

$\sum x = 34.2 \qquad \sum x^2 = 121.6$

Assume that the data can be regarded as a random sample from a normal population.

a For the new repair method, calculate an unbiased estimate of the variance.

b Use your estimate from **a** to calculate for the new repair method a 95% confidence interval for

i the mean,

ii the standard deviation.

c Use your calculations and the given data to compare the two repair methods in order to advise the company as to which method to use.

d Suggest an alternative way of comparing the two methods of repair using the 10 randomly chosen engineers. 

Summary of key points

1 If a random sample of n observations $X_1, X_2, \ldots, X_n$ is selected from a normal distribution with mean μ, and unknown variance σ^2 then

$$\frac{(\bar{X} - \mu)}{\frac{S}{\sqrt{n}}} \sim t_{n-1}$$

where $S^2 = \dfrac{\sum X^2 - n\bar{X}^2}{n - 1}$

2 If the probability of a mean being outside the confidence interval is α then the $100(1 - \alpha)$ confidence limits are given by

$$\bar{x} \pm t_{(n-1)}\frac{\alpha}{2} \times \frac{s}{\sqrt{n}}$$

and the $100(1 - \alpha)$ confidence interval for the mean μ of a normal distribution is:

$$\left(\bar{x} - t_{n-1}\left(\frac{\alpha}{2}\right) \times \frac{s}{\sqrt{n}},\quad \bar{x} + t_{n-1}\left(\frac{\alpha}{2}\right) \times \frac{s}{\sqrt{n}}\right)$$

3 If a random sample of n observations $X_1, X_2, \ldots, X_n$ is selected from $N(\mu, \sigma^2)$ then

$$\frac{(n-1)S^2}{\sigma^2} \sim \chi^2_{n-1}$$

4 If the probability of a variance being outside the confidence interval is α then the $100(1 - \alpha)$ confidence limits are

$$\frac{(n-1)s^2}{\chi^2_{n-1}\left(\frac{\alpha}{2}\right)} \text{ and } \frac{(n-1)s^2}{\chi^2_{n-1}\left(1 - \frac{\alpha}{2}\right)}$$

The $100(1 - \alpha)\%$ confidence interval for the variance of a normal distribution is

$$\left(\frac{(n-1)s^2}{\chi^2_{n-1}\left(\frac{\alpha}{2}\right)}, \frac{(n-1)s^2}{\chi^2_{n-1}\left(1 - \frac{\alpha}{2}\right)}\right)$$

Review Exercise

1 Historical records from a large colony of squirrels show that the weight of squirrels is normally distributed with a mean of 1012 g. Following a change in the diet of squirrels, a biologist is interested in whether or not the mean weight has changed.

A random sample of 14 squirrels is weighed and their weights x, in grams, recorded. The results are summarised as follows:

$$\sum x = 13\,700, \qquad \sum x^2 = 13\,448\,750.$$

Stating your hypotheses clearly test, at the 5% level of significance, whether or not there has been a change in the mean weight of the squirrels. *E*

2 A random sample $X_1, X_2, \ldots, X_{10}$ is taken from a population with mean μ and variance σ^2.

a Determine the bias, if any, of each of the following estimators of μ.

$$\theta_1 = \frac{X_3 + X_4 + X_5}{3}$$

$$\theta_2 = \frac{X_{10} - X_1}{3}$$

$$\theta_3 = \frac{3X_1 + 2X_2 + X_{10}}{6}$$

b Find the variance of each of these estimators.

c State, giving reasons, which of these three estimators for μ *is*

i the best estimator,

ii the worst estimator. *E*

3 A random sample of 10 mustard plants had the following heights, in millimetres, after 4 days growth.

5.0, 4.5, 4.8, 5.2, 4.3, 5.1, 5.2, 4.9, 5.1, 5.0

Those grown previously had a mean height of 5.1 mm after 4 days. Using a 2.5% significance level, test whether or not the mean height of these plants is less than that of those grown previously.

(You may assume that the height of mustard plants after 4 days follows a normal distribution.) *E*

4 A mechanic is required to change car tyres. An inspector timed a random sample of 20 tyre changes and calculated the unbiased estimate of the population variance to be 6.25 minutes^2. Test, at the 5% significance level, whether or not the standard deviation of the population of times taken by the mechanic is greater than 2 minutes. State your hypotheses clearly. *E*

5 The value of orders, in £, made to a firm over the internet has distribution $N(\mu, \sigma^2)$. A random sample of n orders is taken and $\overline{X}$ denotes the sample mean.

a Write down the mean and variance of $\overline{X}$ in terms of μ and σ^2.

A second sample of m orders is taken and $\overline{Y}$ denotes the mean of this sample.

An estimator of the population mean is given by

$$U = \frac{n\overline{X} + m\overline{Y}}{n + m}$$

b Show that U is an unbiased estimator for μ.

c Show that the variance of U is $\dfrac{\sigma^2}{n + m}$

d State which of $\overline{X}$ or U is a better estimator for μ. Give a reason for your answer.

6 A machine is set to fill bags with flour such that the mean weight is 1010 grams.

To check that the machine is working properly, a random sample of 8 bags is selected. The weight of flour, in grams, in each bag is as follows.

1010 1015 1005 1000 998 1008 1012 1007

Carry out a suitable test, at the 5% significance level, to test whether or not the mean weight of flour in the bags is less than 1010 grams. (You may assume that the weight of flour delivered by the machine is normally distributed.)

7 A train company claims that the probability p of one of its trains arriving late is 10%. A regular traveller on the company's trains believes that the probability is greater than 10% and decides to test this by randomly selecting 12 trains and recording the number, X, of trains that were late. The traveller sets up the hypotheses $H_0: p = 0.1$ and $H_1: p > 0.1$ and accepts the null hypothesis if $x \leqslant 2$

a Find the size of the test.

b Show that the power function of the test is

$$1 - (1 - p)^{10}(1 + 10p + 55p^2).$$

c Calculate the power of the test when

i $p = 0.2$ **ii** $p = 0.6$

d Comment on your results from part **c**.

8 It is suggested that a Poisson distribution with parameter λ can model the number of currants in a currant bun. A random bun is selected in order to test the hypotheses $H_0: \lambda = 8$ against $H_1: \lambda \neq 8$, using a 10% level of significance.

a Find the critical region for this test, such that the probability in each tail is as close as possible to 5%.

b Given that $\lambda = 10$, find

i the probability of a type II error,

ii the power of the test.

9 The length X mm of a spring made by a machine is normally distributed $N(\mu, \sigma^2)$. A random sample of 20 springs is selected and their lengths measured in millimetres. Using this sample, the unbiased estimates of μ and σ^2 are

$\bar{x} = 100.6 \qquad s^2 = 1.5$

Stating your hypotheses clearly test, at the 10% level of significance,

a whether or not the variance of the lengths of springs is different from 0.9

b whether or not the mean length of the springs is greater than 100 mm.

10 A town council is concerned that the mean price of renting two bedroom flats in the town has exceeded £650 per month. A random sample of eight two bedroom flats gave the following results, £x, per month.

705, 640, 560, 680, 800, 620, 580, 760

[You may assume $\sum x = 5345$, $\sum x^2 = 3\,621\,025$]

a Find a 90% confidence interval for the mean price of renting a two bedroom flat.

b State an assumption that is required for the validity of your interval in part **a.**

c Comment on whether or not the town council is justified in being concerned. Give a reason for your answer. *E*

11 A technician is trying to estimate the area μ^2 of a metal square. The independent random variables X_1 and X_2 are each distributed $N(\mu, \sigma^2)$ and represent two measurements of the sides of the square. Two estimators of the area, A_1 and A_2, are proposed where

$$A_1 = X_1X_2 \text{ and } A_2 = \left(\frac{X_1 + X_2}{2}\right)^2$$

[You may assume that if X_1 and X_2 are independent random variables then

$$E(X_1X_2) = E(X_1)E(X_2)]$$

a Find $E(A_1)$ and show that

$$E(A_2) = \mu^2 + \frac{\sigma^2}{2}$$

b Find the bias of each of these estimators.

The technician is told that $\text{Var}(A_1) = \sigma^4 + 2\mu^2\sigma^2$ and $\text{Var}(A_2) = \frac{1}{2}\sigma^4 + 2\mu^2\sigma^2$. The technician decided to use A_1 as the estimator for μ^2.

c Suggest a possible reason for this decision.

A statistician suggests taking a random sample of n measurements of sides of the square and finding the mean $\bar{X}$. He knows that $E(\bar{X}^2) = \mu^2 + \frac{\sigma^2}{n}$ and

$$\text{Var}(\bar{X}^2) = \frac{2\sigma^4}{n^2} + \frac{4\sigma^2\mu^2}{n}$$

d Explain whether or not $\bar{X}^2$ is a consistent estimator of μ^2. *E*

12 A random sample of 15 tomatoes is taken and the weight x grams of each tomato is found. The results are summarised by $\sum x = 208$ and $\sum x^2 = 2962$

a Assuming that the weights of the tomatoes are normally distributed, calculate the 90% confidence interval for the variance σ^2 of the weights of the tomatoes.

b State, with a reason, whether or not the confidence interval supports the assertion $\sigma^2 = 3$ *E*

13 a Define

i a type I error,

ii a type II error.

A small aviary, that leaves the eggs with the parent birds, rears chicks at an average rate of 5 per year. In order to increase the number of chicks reared per year it is decided to remove the eggs from the aviary as soon as they are laid and put them in an incubator. At the end of the first year of using an incubator 7 chicks had been successfully reared.

b Assuming that the number of chicks reared per year follows a Poisson distribution test, at the 5% significance level, whether or not there is evidence of an increase in the number of chicks reared per year. State your hypotheses clearly.

c Calculate the probability of the type I error for this test.

d Given that the true average number of chicks reared per year when the eggs are hatched in an incubator is 8, calculate the probability of a type II error. *E*

14 a Explain briefly what you understand by

i an unbiased estimator,

ii a consistent estimator

of an unknown population parameter θ.

From a binomial population, in which the proportion of successes is p, 3 samples of size n are taken. The number of successes X_1, X_2, and X_3 are recorded and used to estimate p.

b Determine the bias, if any, of each of the following estimators of p.

$$\hat{p}_1 = \frac{X_1 + X_2 + X_3}{3n}$$

$$\hat{p}_2 = \frac{X_1 + 3X_2 + X_3}{6n}$$

$$\hat{p}_3 = \frac{2X_1 + 3X_2 + X_3}{6n}$$

c Find the variance of each of these estimators.

d State, giving a reason, which of the three estimators for p is

i the best estimator,

ii the worst estimator. *E*

15 Define

a a type I error, **b** the size of a test.

Jane claims that she can read Alan's mind. To test this claim Alan randomly chooses a card with one of 4 symbols on it. He then concentrates on the symbol. Jane then attempts to read Alan's mind by stating what symbol she thinks is on the card. The experiment is carried out 8 times and the number of times, X, that Jane is correct is recorded.

The probability of Jane stating the correct symbol is denoted by p.

To test the hypothesis H_0: $p = 0.25$ against H_1: $p > 0.25$, a critical region of $X > 6$ is used.

c Find the size of this test.

d Show that the power function of this test is $8p^7 - 7p^8$

Given that $p = 0.3$, calculate

e the power of this test,

f the probability of a type II error.

g Suggest two ways in which you might reduce the probability of a type II error. *E*

16 Rolls of cloth delivered to a factory contain defects at an average rate of λ per metre. A quality assurance manager selects a random sample of 15 metres of cloth from each delivery to test whether or not there is evidence that $\lambda > 0.3$. The criterion that the manager uses for rejecting the hypothesis that $\lambda = 0.3$ is that there are 9 or more defects in the sample.

a Find the size of the test.

Table 1 gives some values, to 2 decimal places, of the power function of this test.

λ	0.4	0.5	0.6	0.7	0.8	0.9	1.0
Power	0.15	0.34	r	0.72	0.85	0.92	0.96

Table 1

b Find the value of r.

The manager would like to design a test, of whether or not $\lambda > 0.3$, that uses a smaller length of cloth. He chooses a length of 10 m and requires the probability of a type I error to be less than 10%.

c Find the criterion to reject the hypothesis that $\lambda = 0.3$ which makes the test as powerful as possible.

d Hence state the size of this second test.

Table 2 gives some values, to 2 decimal places, of the power function for the test in part **c**.

λ	0.4	0.5	0.6	0.7	0.8	0.9	1.0
Power	0.21	0.38	0.55	0.70	s	0.88	0.93

Table 2

e Find the value of s.

f Using the same axes, on graph paper draw the graphs of the power functions of these two tests.

g **i** State the value of λ where the graphs cross.

ii Explain the significance of λ being greater than this value.

The cost of wrongly rejecting a delivery of cloth with $\lambda = 0.3$ is low. Deliveries of cloth with $\lambda > 0.7$ are unusual.

h Suggest, giving your reasons, which the test manager should adopt. *E*

17 The number of tornadoes per year to hit a particular town follows a Poisson distribution with mean λ. A weatherman claims that due to climate changes the mean number of tornadoes per year has decreased. He records the number of tornadoes x to hit the town last year.

To test the hypotheses H_0: $\lambda = 7$ and H_1: $\lambda < 7$, a critical region of $x \leqslant 3$ is used.

a Find, in terms λ the power function of this test.

b Find the size of this test.

c Find the probability of a type II error when $\lambda = 4$ *E*

18 A nutritionist studied the levels of cholesterol, X mg/cm^3, of male students at a large college. She assumed that X was distributed N(μ, σ^2) and examined a random sample of 25 male students. Using this sample she obtained unbiased estimates of μ and σ^2 as

$$\hat{\mu} = 1.68 \qquad \hat{\sigma}^2 = 1.79$$

a Find a 95% confidence interval for μ.

b Obtain a 95% confidence interval for σ^2.

A cholesterol reading of more than 2.5 mg/cm^3 is regarded as high.

c Use appropriate confidence limits from parts **a** and **b** to find the lowest estimate of the proportion of male students in the college with high cholesterol. *E*

19 A random sample of three independent variables X_1, X_2 and X_3 is taken from a distribution with mean μ and variance σ^2.

a Show that $\frac{2}{3}X_1 - \frac{1}{2}X_2 + \frac{5}{6}X_3$ is an unbiased estimator for μ.

An unbiased estimator for μ is given by $\hat{\mu} = aX_1 + bX_2$ where a and b are constants.

b Show that Var ($\hat{\mu}$) = $(2a^2 - 2a + 1)\sigma^2$

c Hence determine the value of a and the value of b for which $\hat{\mu}$ has minimum variance. *E*

20 A supervisor wishes to check the typing speed of a new typist. On 10 randomly selected occasions, the supervisor records the time taken for the new typist to type 100 words. The results, in seconds, are given below.

110 125 130 126 128 127 118
120 122 125

The supervisor assumes that the time taken to type 100 words is normally distributed.

a Calculate a 95% confidence interval for

i the mean,

ii the variance

of the population of times taken by this typist to type 100 words.

The supervisor requires the average time needed to type 100 words to be no more than 130 seconds and the standard deviation to be no more than 4 seconds.

b Comment on whether or not the supervisor should be concerned about the speed of the new typist. *E*

21 A machine is filling bottles of milk. A random sample of 16 bottles was taken and the volume of milk in each bottle was measured and recorded. The volume of milk in a bottle is normally distributed and the unbiased estimate of the variance, s^2, of the volume of milk in a bottle is 0.003

a Find a 95% confidence interval for the variance of the population of volumes of milk from which the sample was taken.

The machine should fill bottles so that the standard deviation of the volumes is equal to 0.07

b Comment on this with reference to your 95% confidence interval. *E*

22 A butter packing machine cuts butter into blocks. The weight of a block of butter is normally distributed with a mean weight of 250 g and a standard deviation of 4 g.

A random sample of 15 blocks is taken to monitor any change in the mean weight of the blocks of butter.

a Find the critical region of a suitable test using a 2% level of significance.

b Assuming the mean weight of a block of butter has increased to 254 g, find the probability of a type II error. *E*

23 A drug is claimed to produce a cure to a certain disease in 35% of people who have the disease. To test this claim a sample of 20 people having this disease is chosen at random and given the drug. If the number of people cured is between 4 and 10 inclusive the claim will be accepted. Otherwise the claim will not be accepted.

a Write down suitable hypotheses to carry out this test.

b Find the probability of making a type I error.

The table below gives the value of the probability of the type II error, to 4 decimal places, for different values of p where p is the probability of the drug curing a person with the disease.

P(cure)	0.2	0.3	0.4	0.5
P(Type II error)	0.5880	r	0.8565	s

c Calculate the value of r and the value of s.

d Calculate the power of the test for $p = 0.2$ and $p = 0.4$

e Comment, giving your reasons, on the suitability of this test procedure. *E*

24 A doctor wishes to study the level of blood glucose in males. The level of blood glucose is normally distributed. The doctor measured the blood glucose of 10 randomly selected male students from a school. The results, in mmol/litre, are given below.

4.7 3.6 3.8 4.7 4.1
2.2 3.6 4.0 4.4 5.0

a Calculate a 95% confidence interval for the mean.

b Calculate a 95% confidence interval for the variance.

A blood glucose reading of more than 7 mmol/litre is counted as high.

c Use appropriate confidence limits from parts **a** and **b** to find the highest estimate of the proportion of male students in the school with a high blood glucose level. *E*

After completing this chapter you should be able to:

- test whether two independent random variables are from normal populations with equal variance
- find a pooled estimate of variance
- find the confidence interval for the difference between two means from independent normal distributions with equal but unknown variances
- conduct a hypothesis test for the difference between the means of two independent normal distributions with equal but unknown variances
- use a paired *t*-test.

Two-sample procedures

A biologist believes that limpets on the north facing side of a rock are smaller than limpets on the south facing side of the rock.

The mean diameter of 15 limpets on the north facing rock is calculated to be 17.23 mm.

The mean diameter of 12 limpets on the south facing rock is calculated to be 21.23 mm.

Is there enough evidence to support the biologist's claim?

You will be able to answer this question when you have done this chapter.

3.1 You need to be able to use the *F*-distribution.

In Chapter 2 you were making deductions about populations by taking a single sample from a normal distribution; this chapter deals with the questions you can ask when two separate random samples are taken from normal distributions.

Suppose that you take a random sample of n_x observations from a $N(\mu_x, \sigma_x^2)$ distribution and independently a random sample of n_y observations from a $N(\mu_y, \sigma_y^2)$ distribution. Unbiased estimators for the two population variances are s_x^2 and s_y^2.

In Section 2.4 you saw that

$$\frac{(n_x - 1)S_x^2}{\sigma_x^2} \sim \chi^2_{n_x - 1} \text{ and } \frac{(n_y - 1)S_y^2}{\sigma_y^2} \sim \chi^2_{n_y - 1}.$$

It follows from this that $\dfrac{\dfrac{(n_x - 1)S_x^2}{\sigma_x^2}}{\dfrac{(n_y - 1)S_y^2}{\sigma_y^2}} \sim \dfrac{\chi^2_{n_x - 1}}{\chi^2_{n_y - 1}}$

so $$\frac{\dfrac{S_x^2}{\sigma_x^2}}{\dfrac{S_y^2}{\sigma_y^2}} \sim \frac{\dfrac{\chi^2_{n_x - 1}}{(n_x - 1)}}{\dfrac{\chi^2_{n_y - 1}}{(n_y - 1)}} \text{ and } \frac{\dfrac{S_y^2}{\sigma_y^2}}{\dfrac{S_x^2}{\sigma_x^2}} \sim \frac{\dfrac{\chi^2_{n_y - 1}}{(n_y - 1)}}{\dfrac{\chi^2_{n_x - 1}}{(n_x - 1)}}.$$

Distributions such as $\dfrac{\dfrac{\chi^2_{n_x - 1}}{(n_x - 1)}}{\dfrac{\chi^2_{n_y - 1}}{(n_y - 1)}}$ were first studied by Sir Ronald Fisher, and are named *F*-distributions in his honour.

The distribution $\dfrac{\dfrac{\chi^2_{n_x - 1}}{(n_x - 1)}}{\dfrac{\chi^2_{n_y - 1}}{(n_y - 1)}}$ has two parameters $(n_x - 1)$ and $(n_y - 1)$ and is usually denoted

by $F_{n_x - 1,\, n_y - 1}$, or by $F_{\nu_1,\, \nu_2}$ where $\nu_1 = (n_x - 1)$ and $\nu_2 = (n_y - 1)$ i.e. if $n_x = 13$ and $n_y = 9$ the distribution would be a $F_{12,\, 8}$-distribution.

A typical distribution is shown opposite.

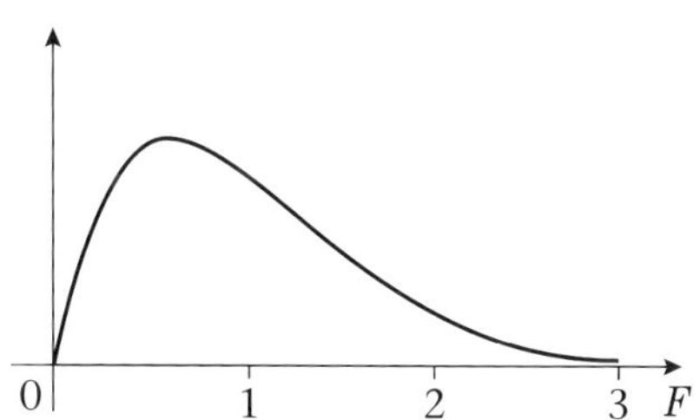

Since variances are always positive F is always greater than zero.

Now if a sample of size n_x is taken from a normal random variable X and a sample of size n_y is taken from a normal random variable Y then

$$\frac{\dfrac{S_x^2}{\sigma_x^2}}{\dfrac{S_y^2}{\sigma_y^2}} \sim F_{n_x - 1,\, n_y - 1} \text{ and } \frac{\dfrac{S_y^2}{\sigma_y^2}}{\dfrac{S_x^2}{\sigma_x^2}} \sim F_{n_y - 1,\, n_x - 1}$$

Since $\dfrac{\frac{S_x^2}{\sigma_x^2}}{\frac{S_y^2}{\sigma_y^2}} \neq \dfrac{\frac{S_y^2}{\sigma_y^2}}{\frac{S_x^2}{\sigma_x^2}}$ it is clear that $F_{n_x - 1, n_y - 1} \neq F_{n_y - 1, n_x - 1}$.

Remember that the order is important. If S_x^2 is at the top of the fraction $\dfrac{\frac{S_x^2}{\sigma_x^2}}{\frac{S_y^2}{\sigma_y^2}}$, then $n_x - 1$ comes first after the F, but if S_y^2 is at the top then $n_y - 1$ comes first.

■ **For a random sample of n_x observations from a $N(\mu_x, \sigma_x^2)$ distribution and an independent random sample of n_y observations from a $N(\mu_y, \sigma_y^2)$ distribution,**

$$\dfrac{\frac{S_x^2}{\sigma_x^2}}{\frac{S_y^2}{\sigma_y^2}} \sim F_{n_x - 1, n_y - 1}$$

3.2 You need to be able to use the *F*-distribution tables.

The *F*-distribution has two parameters $\nu_1 = n_x - 1$ and $\nu_2 = n_y - 1$, and to get all distributions relating to all possible combinations of ν_1 and ν_2 would require very extensive tables.

The numbers of degrees of freedom, ν_1 and ν_2 are used here because that is how they are described on the tables, but ν_x and ν_y could equally well be used.

The *F*-distribution is used mainly in hypothesis testing for variances, and so you are not really interested in all values of F_{ν_1, ν_2}.

The values of F_{ν_1, ν_2} that are of interest are the critical values, which are exceeded with probabilities of 5%, 1% etc. These critical values are written $F_{\nu_1, \nu_2}(0.05)$ or $F_{\nu_1, \nu_2}(0.01)$. $F_{\nu_1, \nu_2}(0.05)$ is illustrated below.

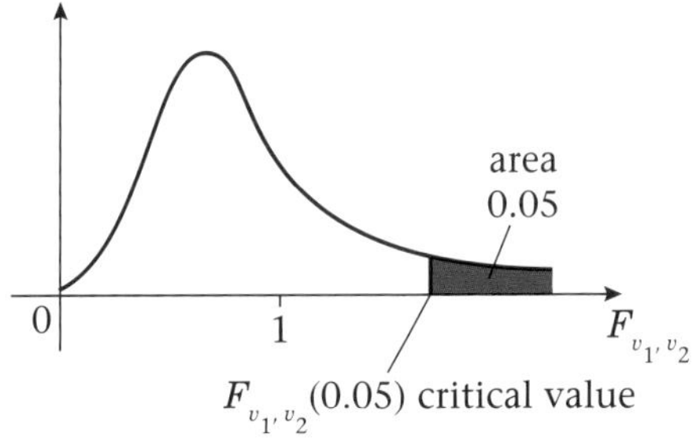

A separate table is given for each significance level (the table on page 111 is for the 1% (0.01) and 5% (0.05) significance levels). The first row at the top gives values of ν_1, (remember that ν_1 comes first after the F), and the first column on the left gives values of ν_2. Where row and column meet gives the critical value corresponding to the significance level of that table. A short extract from the 0.05 significance level table is given on the following page.

Probability	ν_2 / ν_1	1	2	3	4	5	6	8	10	12	24	∞
0.05	1	161.4	199.5	215.7	224.6	230.2	234.0	238.9	241.9	243.9	249.1	254.3
	2	18.51	19.00	19.16	19.25	19.30	19.33	19.37	19.40	19.41	19.46	19.50
	3	10.13	9.55	9.28	9.12	9.01	8.94	8.85	8.79	8.74	8.64	8.53
	4	7.71	6.94	6.59	6.39	6.26	6.16	6.04	5.96	5.91	5.77	5.63
	5	6.61	5.79	5.41	5.19	5.05	4.95	4.82	4.74	4.68	4.53	4.37
	6	5.99	5.14	4.76	4.53	4.39	4.28	4.15	4.06	4.00	3.84	3.67
	7	5.59	4.74	4.35	4.12	3.97	3.87	3.73	3.64	3.57	3.41	3.23
	8	5.32	4.46	4.07	3.84	3.69	3.58	3.44	3.35	3.28	3.12	2.93
	9	5.12	4.26	3.86	3.63	3.48	3.37	3.23	3.14	3.07	2.90	2.71

To find for example the value of $F_{3,7}(0.05)$ you find the intersection of the 3rd column and 7th row.

Example 1

Use the table to find **a** $F_{5,\,8}(0.05)$ critical value. **b** $F_{8,\,5}(0.05)$ critical value.

a $F_{5,\,8}(0.05)$ critical value $= 3.69$

b $F_{8,\,5}(0.05)$ critical value $= 4.82$

Using the table the critical value at the 5% level for $F_{5,\,8}$ is at the intersection of the 5th column and the 8th row.

The critical value of $F_{8,\,5}$ is at the intersection of the 8th column and the 5th row.

The 5% probability table enables you to read off for different values of ν_1 and ν_2 the value of $F_{\nu_1,\,\nu_2}$ that is exceeded with probability 0.05 (the $F_{\nu_1,\,\nu_2}(0.05)$ upper critical value).

The 1% probability table enables you to read off for different values of ν_1 and ν_2 the value of $F_{\nu_1,\,\nu_2}$ that is exceeded with probability 0.01 (the $F_{\nu_1,\,\nu_2}(0.01)$ upper critical value).

The table can also be used to find a value of $F_{\nu_1,\,\nu_2}$ that is exceeded with probability 0.95 or, looking at it a different way, a value of $F_{\nu_1,\,\nu_2}$ such that the probability of getting a lower value of $F_{\nu_1,\,\nu_2}$ is 0.05, (the $F_{\nu_1,\,\nu_2}(0.95)$ lower critical value). The region is shown opposite.

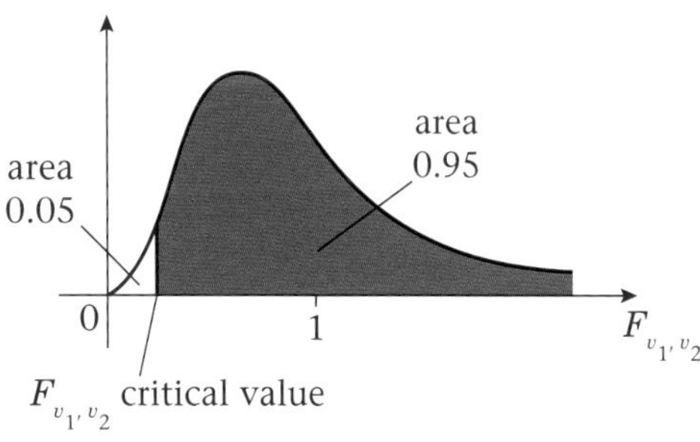

It is done in the following way

$$P(F_{\nu_1,\,\nu_2} < f) = P\left(\frac{\frac{\chi^2_{\nu_1}}{\nu_1}}{\frac{\chi^2_{\nu_2}}{\nu_2}} < f\right)$$

$$= P\left(\frac{1}{f} < \frac{\frac{\chi^2_{\nu_2}}{\nu_2}}{\frac{\chi^2_{\nu_1}}{\nu_1}}\right)$$

$$= P\left(\frac{1}{f} < F_{\nu_2,\,\nu_1}\right)$$

Notice that the degrees of freedom are interchanged when using a reciprocal to find the lower percentage point.

Therefore

$$F_{\nu_1, \nu_2}(0.95) \text{ lower critical value} = \frac{1}{F_{\nu_2, \nu_1}(0.05) \text{ upper critical value}}.$$

We usually use the following

- $F_{\nu_2, \nu_1} = \dfrac{1}{F_{\nu_1, \nu_2}}$

Example 2

Find critical values for

a $F_{8, 10}(0.95)$

b $F_{10, 8}(0.95)$

a $F_{8, 10}(0.95)$ critical value $= \dfrac{1}{3.35}$

$= 0.2985$

$= 0.30$ (2 d.p.)

Using $\dfrac{1}{F_{10, 8}(0.05) \text{ critical value}}$.

b $F_{10, 8}(0.95)$ critical value $= \dfrac{1}{3.07}$

$= 0.33$ (2 d.p.)

Using $\dfrac{1}{F_{8, 10}(0.05) \text{ critical value}}$.

Example 3

Find the lower and upper 5% critical value for an $F_{a,b}$-distribution in each of the following cases:

a $a = 6, b = 10$

b $a = 12, b = 8$.

a The upper critical value is $F_{6, 10}(0.05) = 3.22$

The lower 5% critical value is $F_{6, 10}(0.95) = \dfrac{1}{F_{10, 6}} = \dfrac{1}{4.06} = 0.25$

b The upper critical value is $F_{12, 8}(0.05) = 3.28$

The lower 5% critical value is $F_{12, 8}(0.95) = \dfrac{1}{F_{8, 12}} = \dfrac{1}{2.85} = 0.35$

Example 4

The random variable X follows an F-distribution with 8 and 10 degrees of freedom.

Find $\text{P}\left(\dfrac{1}{5.81} < X < 5.06\right)$

Looking at the upper tail $P(X > 5.06) = P(F_{8,10} > 5.06)$

$P(X > 5.06) = 0.01$

$P(X < 5.06) = 1 - 0.01 = 0.99$

From the tables $F_{8,\,10}(5\%) = 3.07$ and $F_{8,\,10}(1\%) = 5.06$

Looking at the other tail $P\left(X < \frac{1}{5.81}\right) = P\left(F_{8,10} < \frac{1}{5.81}\right)$

$= P(F_{10,\,8} > 5.81)$

Using $P(F_{\nu_1,\,\nu_2} < f) = P\left(\frac{1}{f} < F_{\nu_2,\,\nu_1}\right)$.

$\therefore$ $P\left(X < \frac{1}{5.81}\right) = 0.01$

From the tables $F_{10,\,8}(5\%) = 3.35$ and $F_{10,\,8}(1\%) = 5.81$

Now $P\left(\frac{1}{5.81} < X < 5.06\right) = P(X < 5.06) - P\left(X < \frac{1}{5.81}\right)$

$= 0.99 - 0.01$

$= 0.98$

Example 5

The random variable X follows a $F_{6,\,12}$-distribution. Find $P(X < 0.25)$.

$P(X < 0.25) = P(F_{6,\,12} < 0.25) = P\left(F_{12,\,6} > \frac{1}{0.25}\right)$

$= P(F_{12,\,6} > 4)$

From the tables $F_{12,\,6}(0.05) = 4$

$\therefore$ $P(F_{12,\,6} > 4) = P(F_{6,\,12} < 0.25) = 0.05$

Exercise 3A

1 Find the upper 5% critical value for a $F_{a,b}$-distribution in each of the following cases:

a $a = 12, b = 18$, **b** $a = 4, b = 11$, **c** $a = 6, b = 9$.

2 Find the lower 5% critical value for a $F_{a,b}$-distribution in each of the following cases:

a $a = 6, b = 8$, **b** $a = 25, b = 12$, **c** $a = 5, b = 5$.

3 Find the upper 1% critical value for a $F_{a,b}$-distribution in each of the following cases:

a $a = 12, b = 18$, **b** $a = 6, b = 16$, **c** $a = 5, b = 9$.

4 Find the lower 1% critical value for a $F_{a,b}$-distribution in each of the following cases:

a $a = 3, b = 12$, **b** $a = 8, b = 12$, **c** $a = 5, b = 12$.

5 Find the lower and upper 5% critical value for a $F_{a,b}$-distribution in each of the following cases:

a $a = 8, b = 10$, **b** $a = 12, b = 10$, **c** $a = 3, b = 5$.

6 The random variable X follows a $F_{40, 12}$-distribution.
Find $P(X < 0.5)$.

7 The random variable X follows a $F_{12, 8}$-distribution.

Find $P\left(\frac{1}{2.85} < X < 3.28\right)$

8 The random variable X has an F-distribution with 2 and 7 degrees of freedom.
Find $P(X < 9.55)$.

9 The random variable X follows an F-distribution with 6 and 12 degrees of freedom.

a Show that $P(0.25 < X < 3.00) = 0.9$

A large number of values are randomly selected from an F-distribution with 6 and 12 degrees of freedom.

b Find the probability that the seventh value to be selected will be the third value to lie between 0.25 and 3.00

3.3 You need to be able to test whether two independent random samples are from normal populations with equal variances.

Customers in supermarkets expect the produce that they buy loose, e.g. potatoes, apples, etc. to be of a uniform size. When purchasing from suppliers, therefore, the managers of supermarkets are concerned not only with the mean size of the produce but also how variable that size is. Given two suppliers the one selected is likely to be the one whose produce has the lowest variance. 'How', you might ask, 'is the manager to tell if one variance is larger than the other, simply by taking a sample from each?' The following test is designed for such cases.

You begin by making the assumptions that the samples are drawn from independent normal populations.

If you have two random samples of sizes n_x and n_y respectively then, from Section 3.1,

$$\frac{\frac{S_x^2}{\sigma_x^2}}{\frac{S_y^2}{\sigma_y^2}} \sim F_{n_x - 1,\, n_y - 1}$$

If you assume that $\sigma_x^2 = \sigma_y^2$, then $\frac{\sigma_y^2}{\sigma_x^2} = 1$ and

$$\frac{S_x^2}{S_y^2} \sim F_{n_x - 1,\, n_y - 1}$$

- **If a random sample of n_x observations is taken from a normal distribution with unknown variance σ^2 and an independent random sample of n_y observations is taken from a normal distribution with equal but unknown variance then**

$$\frac{S_x^2}{S_y^2} \sim F_{n_x - 1,\, n_y - 1}$$

If $\sigma_x^2 = \sigma_y^2$ then you would expect $\frac{S_x^2}{S_y^2}$ to be close to 1, but if $\sigma_x^2 > \sigma_y^2$ then you would expect it to be much greater than 1

You wish to test the hypothesis $H_0: \sigma_x^2 = \sigma_y^2$ against the alternative hypothesis $\sigma_x^2 > \sigma_y^2$.

As before when testing hypotheses, if your value of $\frac{S_x^2}{S_y^2}$ is such that it could only occur under the null hypothesis with a probability $\leqslant \alpha$ (typically $\alpha = 0.05$) then you reject the null hypothesis; otherwise you have to conclude that there is insufficient evidence to reject the null hypothesis. The critical value $F_{\nu_x, \nu_y}(\alpha)$ can be read from the table.

To test whether two variances are the same a simple set of rules can be followed.

1 Find s_l^2 and s_s^2, the larger and smaller variances respectively.

2 Write down the null hypothesis $H_0: \sigma_l^2 = \sigma_s^2$.

3 Write down the alternative hypothesis $H_1: \sigma_l^2 > \sigma_s^2$ (one-tailed), or $H_1: \sigma_l^2 \neq \sigma_s^2$ (two-tailed).

4 Look up the critical value of F_{ν_l, ν_s} where ν_l is the number of degrees of freedom of the distribution with the larger variance and ν_s is the number of degrees of freedom of the distribution with the smaller variance. If a two-tailed test is used, α is halved (e.g. for a 10% significance level you would use $F_{\nu_l, \nu_s}(5\%)$ as the critical value).

5 Write down the critical region.

6 Calculate $F_{\text{test}} = \frac{s_l^2}{s_s^2}$

7 See whether or not F_{test} lies in the critical region or not and draw your conclusions. Relate these to the original problem.

Example 6

Two samples of size 13 and 9 are taken from normal distributions X and Y. The two samples give values $s_x^2 = 24$ and $s_y^2 = 18$. Test, at the 5% level, whether or not the variances of the populations from which the samples are drawn are the same by testing $H_0: \sigma_x^2 = \sigma_y^2$ against the alternative hypothesis $H_1: \sigma_x^2 > \sigma_y^2$.

$\nu_l = 13 - 1 = 12$, $\nu_s = 9 - 1 = 8$ — X has the largest variance.

$s_l^2 = 24$ and $s_s^2 = 18$

The critical value is $F_{12, 8}(5\%) = 3.28$ — This is the intersection of the 12th column and the 8th row in the table.

The test statistic is $\frac{s_l^2}{s_s^2} = \frac{24}{18} = 1.33$ — The largest variance is divided by the smallest.

$1.33 < 3.28$

There is insufficient evidence to reject H_0, the two populations have equal variances. — Always state whether you accept or reject H_0 and draw a conclusion (in context if possible).

Example 7

Two samples of size 7 and 11 are taken from normal distributions X and Y. The two samples give values $s_x^2 = 5$ and $s_y^2 = 25$. Test at the 5% level of significance whether or not the variances of the populations from which the samples are drawn are the same by testing $H_0: \sigma_x^2 = \sigma_y^2$ against the alternative hypothesis $H_1: \sigma_x^2 < \sigma_y^2$.

$\nu_l = 11 - 1 = 10, \quad \nu_s = 7 - 1 = 6$ — Y has the largest variance.

$s_l^2 = 25$ and $s_s^2 = 5$

The critical value is $F_{10,6}(5\%) = 4.06$

The test statistic is $\frac{s_l^2}{s_s^2} = \frac{25}{5} = 5$ — The largest variance is divided by the smallest.

$5 > 4.06$

There is sufficient evidence to reject H_0. So $\sigma_x^2 < \sigma_y^2$.

Example 8

Two samples of size 11 and 13 are taken from normal distributions X and Y. The two samples give values $s_x^2 = 1.6$ and $s_y^2 = 2.4$. Test, at the 10% level of significance, whether or not the variances of the populations from which the samples are drawn are equal by testing $H_0: \sigma_x^2 = \sigma_y^2$ against the alternative hypothesis $H_1: \sigma_x^2 \neq \sigma_y^2$.

$\nu_l = 13 - 1 = 12, \quad \nu_s = 11 - 1 = 10,$ — Y has the largest variance.

$s_l^2 = 2.4$ and $s_s^2 = 1.6$

The critical value is $F_{12,10}(5\%) = 2.91$ — Two-tailed test so use $F_{\nu_l,\nu_s}\left(\frac{\alpha}{2}\right)$.

The test statistic is $\frac{s_l^2}{s_s^2} = \frac{2.4}{1.6} = 1.5$

$1.5 < 2.91$

There is insufficient evidence to reject H_0; the two variances are equal. — Always state whether you accept or reject H_0 and draw a conclusion (in context if possible).

Example 9

A manufacturer of wooden furniture stores some of its wood outside and some inside a special store. It is believed that the wood stored inside should have less variable hardness properties than that stored outside. A random sample of 25 pieces of wood stored outside was taken and compared to a random sample of 21 similar pieces taken from the inside store, with the following results

	Outside	Inside
Sample size	25	21
Mean hardness (coded units)	110	122
Sum of squares about the mean	5190	3972

a Test, at the 0.05 level of significance, whether or not the manufacturer's belief is correct.

b State an assumption you have made in order to do this test.

a $s^2_{\text{outside}} = \dfrac{5190}{24} = 216.25$ and $s^2_{\text{inside}} = \dfrac{3972}{20} = 198.6$

$s^2 = \dfrac{\sum(x_i - \bar{x})^2}{n - 1}$

$\nu_o = 25 - 1 = 24, \quad \nu_i = 21 - 1 = 20$

Outside has the largest variance.

$H_0: \sigma_o^2 = \sigma_i^2, \quad H_1: \sigma_o^2 > \sigma_i^2$

critical value $= F_{24, 20}(0.05) = 2.08$

One-tailed test.

$F_{test} = \dfrac{216.25}{198.6} = 1.089$

$1.089 < 2.08$, so there is insufficient evidence to reject H_0; wood stored inside is just as variable in hardness as wood stored outside.

Always state whether you accept or reject H_0 and draw a conclusion (in context if possible).

b The assumption made is that the populations are normally distributed.

Exercise 3B

1 Random samples are taken from two normally distributed populations. There are 11 observations from the first population and the best estimate for the population variance is $s^2 = 7.6$. There are 7 observations from the second population and the best estimate for the population variance is $s^2 = 6.4$

Test, at the 5% level of significance, the hypothesis $H_0: \sigma_1^2 = \sigma_2^2$ against the alternative hypothesis $H_1: \sigma_1^2 > \sigma_2^2$.

2 Random samples are taken from two normally distributed populations. There are 25 observations from the first population and the best estimate for the population variance is $s^2 = 0.42$. There are 41 observations from the second population and the best estimate for the population variance is $s^2 = 0.17$

Test, at the 1% significance level, the hypothesis $H_0: \sigma_1^2 = \sigma_2^2$ against the alternative hypothesis $H_1: \sigma_1^2 > \sigma_2^2$.

3 The variance of the lengths of a sample of 9 tent-poles produced by a machine was 63 mm^2. A second machine produced a sample of 13 tent-poles with a variance of 225 mm^2. Both these values are unbiased estimates of the population variances.

a Test, at the 10% level, whether there is evidence that the machines differ in variability, stating the null and alternative hypotheses.

b State the assumption you have made about the distribution of the populations in order to carry out the test in part **a**.

E

4 Random samples are taken from two normally distributed populations. The size of the sample from the first population is $n_1 = 13$ and this gives an unbiased estimate for the population variance $s_1^2 = 36.4$. The figures for the second population are $n_2 = 9$ and $s_2^2 = 52.6$

Test, at the 5% significance level, whether $\sigma_1^2 = \sigma_2^2$ or if $\sigma_2^2 > \sigma_1^2$.

5 Dining chairs Ltd are in the process of selecting a make of glue for using on the joints of their furniture. There are two possible contenders – Goodstick which is the more expensive, and Holdtight, the cheaper of the two.

The company are concerned that, while both glues are said to have the same adhesive power, one might be more variable than the other.

A series of trials are carried out with each glue and the joints tested to destruction. The force in newtons at which each joint failed is recorded. The results are as follows:

Goodstick	10.3	8.2	9.5	9.9	11.4	
Holdtight	9.6	10.8	9.9	10.8	10.0	10.2

a Test, at the 10% significance level, whether or not the variances are equal.

b Which glue would you recommend and why?

6 The closing balances, £x, of a number of randomly chosen bank current accounts of two different types, Chegrit and Dicabalk, are analysed by a statistician. The summary statistics are given in the table below.

	Sample size	$\sum x$	$\sum x^2$
Chegrit	7	276	143 742
Dicabalk	15	394	102 341

Stating clearly your hypotheses test, at the 10% significance level, whether or not the two distributions have the same variance. (You may assume that the closing balances of each type of account are normally distributed.) **E**

7 Bigborough council wishes to change the bulbs in their traffic lights at regular intervals so that there is a very small probability that any light bulb will fail in service.

The council are anxious that the length of time between changes should be as long as possible, and to this end they have obtained a sample of bulbs from another manufacturer, who claims the same bulb life as their present manufacturer. The council wishes therefore to select the manufacturer whose bulbs have the smallest variance.

When they last tested a random sample of 9 bulbs from their present supplier the summary results were $\sum x = 9415$ hours, $\sum x^2 = 9\,863\,681$, where x represents the lifetime of a bulb.

A random sample of 8 bulbs from the prospective new supplier gave the following bulb lifetimes in hours: 1002, 1018, 943, 1030, 984, 963, 1048, 994

a Calculate unbiased estimates for the means and variances of the two populations.

Assuming that the lifetimes of bulbs are normally distributed,

b test, at the 10% significance level, whether or not the two variances are equal.

c State your recommendation to the council, giving reasons for your choice.

3.4 You need to be able to find a pooled estimate of variance.

Suppose that you take random samples from random variables X and Y that have a common variance σ^2. You will have two estimates of σ^2, namely $s_x{}^2$ and $s_y{}^2$. A better estimate of σ^2 than either $s_x{}^2$ or $s_y{}^2$ can be obtained by pooling the two estimates. The question is 'How should this be done?'

You will recall that for a single sample an unbiased estimate of the population variance was obtained by dividing the total sum of squares of the sample by the number of degrees of freedom. Thus

$$s^2 = \frac{\sum(x - \bar{x})^2}{n - 1}$$

is an unbiased estimate of the variance of the population.

A similar idea works for two pooled estimates. You have

$$s_x{}^2 = \frac{\sum(x - \bar{x}_x)^2}{n_x - 1} \quad \text{and} \quad s_y{}^2 = \frac{\sum(x - \bar{x}_y)^2}{n_y - 1}$$

so that $(n_x - 1)\, s_x{}^2 = \sum(x - \bar{x}_x)^2$ and $(n_y - 1)\, s_y{}^2 = \sum(x - \bar{x}_y)^2$.

Adding these two sums of squares together to get a total sum of squares gives

$$\sum(x - \bar{x}_x)^2 + \sum(x - \bar{x}_y)^2 = (n_x - 1)\, s_x{}^2 + (n_y - 1)\, s_y{}^2,$$

and this will have $(n_x - 1) + (n_y - 1)$ degrees of freedom.

Treating the combined samples as a single sample and dividing the total sum of squares by the number of degrees of freedom gives a pooled estimate, $s_p{}^2$, of σ^2 thus

$$s_p{}^2 = \frac{(n_x - 1)s_x{}^2 + (n_y - 1)s_y{}^2}{(n_x - 1) + (n_y - 1)} = \frac{(n_x - 1)s_x{}^2 + (n_y - 1)s_y{}^2}{n_x + n_y - 2}$$

- **If a random sample of n_x observations is taken from a normal distribution with unknown variance σ^2 and an independent sample of n_y observations is taken from a normal distribution that also has unknown variance σ^2 then a pooled estimate for σ^2 is**

  $$s_p{}^2 = \frac{(n_x - 1)s_x{}^2 + (n_y - 1)s_y{}^2}{n_x + n_y - 2}$$

  where $s_x{}^2 = \dfrac{\sum x^2 - n_x\bar{x}^2}{n_x - 1}$ **and** $s_y{}^2 = \dfrac{\sum y^2 - n_y\bar{y}^2}{n_y - 1}$

Notice that if $n_x = n_y = n$ this reduces to

$$s_p{}^2 = \frac{(n - 1)(s_x{}^2 + s_y{}^2)}{2(n - 1)} = \frac{s_x{}^2 + s_y{}^2}{2}$$

which is the mean of the two variances. The pooled estimate of variance is really a weighted mean of two variances with the two weights being $(n_x - 1)$ and $(n_y - 1)$.

We can show that S_p^2 is an unbiased estimator as follows:

$$\begin{aligned} E[(n_x - 1)S_x^2 + (n_y - 1)S_y^2] &= E[(n_x - 1)S_x^2] + E[(n_y - 1)S_y^2] \\ &= (n_x - 1)\,\sigma^2 + (n_y - 1)\,\sigma^2 \\ &= [(n_x - 1) + (n_y - 1)]\,\sigma^2 \end{aligned}$$

$$\text{so } E(S_p^2) = E\left[\frac{(n_x - 1)S_x^2 + (n_y - 1)S_y^2}{(n_x - 1) + (n_y - 1)}\right]$$

$$= \frac{E[(n_x - 1)S_x^2 + (n_y - 1)S_y^2]}{[(n_x - 1) + (n_y - 1)]}$$

$$= \frac{[(n_x - 1) + (n_y - 1)]\sigma^2}{[(n_x - 1) + (n_y - 1)]}$$

$$= \sigma^2$$

Example 10

A random sample of 15 observations is taken from a population and gives an unbiased estimate for the population variance of 9.47. A second random sample of 12 observations is taken from a different population that has the same population variance as the first population, and gives an unbiased estimate for the variance as 13.84. Calculate an unbiased estimate of the population variance σ^2.

$$s_p^2 = \frac{(14 \times 9.47) + (11 \times 13.84)}{14 + 11}$$

$$= 11.3928$$

Using $s_p^2 = \dfrac{(n_x - 1)s_x^2 + (n_y - 1)s_y^2}{(n_x - 1) + (n_y - 1)}$

3.5 You need to be able to find a confidence interval for the difference between two means from independent normal distributions with equal but unknown variances.

You have already seen that if the sample sizes are large then

$$\frac{(\bar{X} - \bar{Y}) - (\mu_x - \mu_y)}{\sqrt{\dfrac{S_x^2}{n_x} + \dfrac{S_y^2}{n_y}}} \approx N(0, 1^2)$$

When the sample sizes are small you need to make three assumptions:

1 that the populations are normal,

2 that the samples are independent,

3 that the variances of the two samples are equal.

In general, the third assumption is not an unreasonable one to make. In any case, the equality of the variances can be tested using an *F*-test as in Section 3.3.

The third assumption enables you to use an estimator for the common variance, by pooling the two variances as in Section 3.4 to give:

$$S_p^2 = \frac{(n_x - 1)S_x^2 + (n_y - 1)S_y^2}{(n_x - 1) + (n_y - 1)}$$

Substituting S_p^2 for S_x^2 and S_y^2 gives

$$\frac{(\overline{X} - \overline{Y}) - (\mu_x - \mu_y)}{\sqrt{\frac{S_p^2}{n_x} + \frac{S_p^2}{n_y}}} = \frac{(\overline{X} - \overline{Y}) - (\mu_x - \mu_y)}{S_p\sqrt{\frac{1}{n_x} + \frac{1}{n_y}}}$$

Now, because the sample sizes are small, this will not as before follow a $N(0, 1^2)$ distribution.

You have already seen that in the single-sample case

$$\frac{X - \mu_x}{\frac{S}{\sqrt{n_x}}}$$

follows a *t*-distribution, so you will not be surprised to find that

$$\frac{(\overline{X} - \overline{Y}) - (\mu_x - \mu_y)}{S_p\sqrt{\frac{1}{n_x} + \frac{1}{n_y}}}$$

also follows a *t*-distribution.

There are $(n_x + n_y)$ in the total sample and two calculated restrictions (namely the means $\overline{X}$ and $\overline{Y}$), so the number of degrees of freedom will be $n_x + n_y - 2$

- **If a random sample of n_x observations is taken from a normal distribution that has unknown variance σ^2 and an independent sample of n_y observations is taken from a normal distribution with equal variance, then**

$$\frac{(\overline{X} - \overline{Y}) - (\mu_x - \mu_y)}{S_p\sqrt{\frac{1}{n_x} + \frac{1}{n_y}}} \sim t_{n_x + n_y - 2} \text{ where } S_p^2 = \frac{(n_x - 1)S_x^2 + (n_y - 1)S_y^2}{n_x + n_y - 2}$$

As before with confidence intervals you normally expect the interval to be symmetrical, so you split the remainder between the two tails. For example, if you wish to have a 95% interval, the remaining 5% is split equally between the two tails to give $2\frac{1}{2}$% at each tail.

The tables will then give you the value of *t* that is exceeded with 2.5% probability (or 5% for a 90% confidence interval). If you write t_c for the relevant value then

$$P(-t_c < t_{n_x + n_y - 2} < t_c) = 0.95 \text{ (or } 0.90)$$

$$P\left(-t_c < \frac{(\overline{x} - \overline{y}) - (\mu_x - \mu_y)}{s_p\sqrt{\frac{1}{n_x} + \frac{1}{n_y}}} < t_c\right) = 0.95 \text{ (or } 0.90)$$

$$P\left(-t_c\, s_p\sqrt{\frac{1}{n_x} + \frac{1}{n_y}} < (\overline{x} - \overline{y}) - (\mu_x - \mu_y) < t_c\, s_p\sqrt{\frac{1}{n_x} + \frac{1}{n_y}}\right) = 0.95 \text{ (or } 0.90)$$

The confidence limits for $(\mu_x - \mu_y)$ are therefore given by

$$(\bar{x} - \bar{y}) \pm t_c\, s_p\sqrt{\frac{1}{n_x} + \frac{1}{n_y}},$$

and the confidence interval is

$$\left\{(\bar{x} - \bar{y}) - t_c\, s_p\sqrt{\frac{1}{n_x} + \frac{1}{n_y}},\ (\bar{x} - \bar{y}) + t_c\, s_p\sqrt{\frac{1}{n_x} + \frac{1}{n_y}}\right\}$$

- **The confidence limits for the difference between two means from independent normal distributions, X and Y, when the variances are equal but unknown are given by:**

  $$(\bar{x} - \bar{y}) \pm t_c\, s_p\sqrt{\frac{1}{n_x} + \frac{1}{n_y}}$$

  where s_p is the pooled estimate of the population variance, and t_c is the relevant value taken from the t-distribution tables.

  The confidence interval is given by:

  $$\left\{(\bar{x} - \bar{y}) - t_c\, s_p\sqrt{\frac{1}{n_x} + \frac{1}{n_y}},\ (\bar{x} - \bar{y}) + t_c\, s_p\sqrt{\frac{1}{n_x} + \frac{1}{n_y}}\right\}$$

Example 11

In a survey on the petrol consumption of cars a random sample of 12 cars with 2 litre engines was compared with a random sample of 15 cars with 1.6 litre engines. The following results show the consumption, in suitable units of the cars:

2 litre cars: 34.4, 32.1, 30.1, 32.8, 31.5, 35.8, 28.2, 26.6, 28.8, 28.5, 33.6, 28.8

1.6 litre cars: 35.3, 34.0, 36.7, 40.9, 34.4, 39.8, 33.6, 36.7, 34.0, 39.2, 39.8, 38.7, 40.8, 35.0, 36.7

Calculate a 95% confidence interval for the difference between the two mean petrol consumption figures. You may assume that the variables are normally distributed and that they have the same variance.

For the 2 litre engine $n_y = 12$, $\bar{y} = 30.933$, $s_y^2 = 8.177$

For the 1.6 litre engine $n_x = 15$, $\bar{x} = 37.04$, $s_x^2 = 6.894$

$$s_p^2 = \frac{(14 \times 6.894) + (11 \times 8.177)}{25}$$

$\dfrac{(n_x - 1)s_x^2 + (n_y - 1)s_y^2}{n_x + n_y - 2}$

$$= 7.459$$

$\nu = 12 + 15 - 2 = 25$

$$s_p = \sqrt{7.459} = 2.731$$

$t_c = t_{25}\,(2.5\%) = 2.060$

The confidence limits are

Using $(\bar{x} - \bar{y}) \pm t_c\, s_p\sqrt{\frac{1}{n_x} + \frac{1}{n_y}}$

$$(37.04 - 30.933) \pm 2.060 \times 2.731\sqrt{\tfrac{1}{15} + \tfrac{1}{12}} = 6.107 \pm 2.179$$

$$= 8.286 \text{ and } 3.928$$

The 95% confidence interval is (3.928, 8.286) or (3.93, 8.29) to 3 s.f.

Exercise 3C

1 A random sample of 10 toothed winkles was taken from a sheltered shore, and a sample of 15 was taken from a non-sheltered shore. The maximum basal width, (x mm), of the shells was measured and the results are summarised below.

Sheltered shore: $\bar{x} = 25$, $s^2 = 4$ Non-sheltered shore: $\bar{x} = 22$, $s^2 = 5.3$

a Find a 95% confidence interval for the difference between the means.

b State an assumption that you have made when calculating this interval.

2 A packet of plant seeds was sown and, when the seeds had germinated and begun to grow, 8 were transferred into pots containing a soil-less compost and 10 were grown on in a soil-based compost. After 6 weeks of growth the heights, x, in cm of the plants were measured with the following results:

Soil-less compost: 9.3, 8.7, 7.8, 10.0, 9.2, 9.5, 7.9, 8.9

Soil-based compost: 12.8, 13.1, 11.2, 10.1, 13.1, 12.0, 12.5, 11.7, 11.9, 12.0

Assuming that the populations are normally distributed, and that there is a difference between the two means calculate a 90% confidence interval for this difference.

3 Forty children were randomly selected from all 12-year-old children in a large city to compare two methods of teaching the spelling of 50 words which were likely to be unfamiliar to the children. Twenty children were randomly allocated to each method. Six weeks later the children were tested to see how many of the words they could spell correctly. The summary statistics for the two methods are given in the table below, where $\bar{x}$ is the mean number of words spelt correctly, s^2 is an unbiased estimate of the variance of the number of words spelt correctly and n is the number of children taught using each method.

	$\bar{x}$	s^2	n
Method A	32.7	6.1^2	20
Method B	38.2	5.2^2	20

a Calculate a 99% confidence interval for the difference between the mean numbers of words spelt correctly by children who used Method B and Method A.

b State two assumptions you have made in carrying out part **a**.

c Interpret your result. *E*

4 The table below shows summary statistics for the mean daily consumption of cigarettes by a random sample of 10 smokers before and after their attendance at an anti-smoking workshop with $\bar{x}$ representing the means and s^2 representing the unbiased estimates of population variance in each case.

	$\bar{x}$	s^2	n
Mean daily consumption before the workshop	18.6	32.488	10
Mean daily consumption after the workshop	14.3	33.344	10

Stating clearly any assumption you make, calculate a 90% confidence interval for the difference in the mean daily consumption of cigarettes before and after the workshop.

3.6 You need to be able to carry out a hypothesis test for the difference between the means of two independent normal distributions with unknown variances (two-sample *t*-test).

Apart from using the *t*-distribution rather than the normal distribution for finding the critical values, testing the difference between means of two independent normal distributions with unknown variances follows similar steps to those used for testing the difference of means when the variances were known.

The following steps might help you in answering questions on the difference of means of normal distributions when the variances are unknown.

1 Write down H_0.

2 Write down H_1.

3 Specify the significance level α.

4 Write down the number of degrees of freedom ν.

5 Write down the critical region.

6 Calculate the sample means and variances $\bar{x}, \bar{y}, S_x^2$ and S_y^2.

7 Calculate a pooled estimate of the variance:

$$S_p^2 = \frac{(n_x - 1)S_x^2 + (n_y - 1)S_y^2}{n_x + n_y - 2}$$

8 Calculate the value of t:

$$t = \frac{(\bar{X} - \bar{Y}) - (\mu_x - \mu_y)}{S_p\sqrt{\frac{1}{n_x} + \frac{1}{n_y}}}$$

9 Complete the test and state your conclusions. The following points should be addressed:
i is the result significant?
ii what are the implications in terms of the original problem?

Example 12

Two groups of students X and Y were taught by different teachers. At the end of their course a random sample of students from each class was selected and given a test. The test results out of 50 were as follows:

Group X	40	37	45	34	30	41	42	43	36
Group Y	38	43	36	45	35	44	41		

The head teacher wishes to find out if there is a significant difference between the results for these two groups.

a Write down any assumptions that need to be made in order to conduct a difference of means test on this data.

b Assuming that these assumptions apply test, at the 10% level of significance, whether or not there is a significant difference between the means.

a The assumptions that need to be made are that that the two samples come from normal distributions, are independent and that the populations from which they are taken have the same variances.

b $H_0: \mu_x = \mu_y \qquad H_1: \mu_x \neq \mu_y.$

Significance level = 0.05 (two-tailed test)

$$\nu = 9 + 7 - 2 = 14$$

Critical value t_{14} (5%) is 1.761

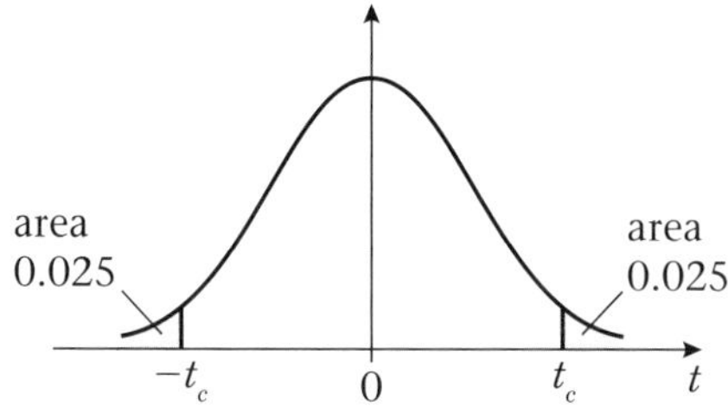

The critical regions are $t \leqslant -1.761$ and $t \geqslant 1.761$

Using a calculator gives $n_x = 9$, $\bar{x} = 38.667$, $S_x^2 = 23.0$, $n_y = 7$, $\bar{y} = 40.286$, $S_y^2 = 15.9$

$$S_p^2 = \frac{(8 \times 23.0) + (6 \times 15.9)}{9 + 7 - 2}$$

$$= 19.957$$

So $S_p = 4.467$

$$t = \frac{40.286 - 38.667}{4.467\sqrt{\frac{1}{9} + \frac{1}{7}}}$$

$$= 0.719$$

$-1.761 < 0.719 < 1.761$ so the result is not significant. Accept H_0. On the evidence given by the two samples there is no difference between the means of the two groups.

1 State your hypotheses.

2 Write down the significance level.

3 Find the number of degrees of freedom ($n_1 + n_2 - 2$ in this case).

4 Look up the critical value in the table.

5 Write down the critical region. There are two regions as it is a two-tailed test.

6 Calculate $\bar{x}$, $\bar{y}$, S_x^2 and S_y^2.

7 Calculate a pooled estimate of the variance using

$$\frac{(n_x - 1)S_x^2 + (n_y - 1)S_y^2}{n_x + n_y - 2}$$

8 Calculate t using

$$\frac{|(\bar{x} - \bar{y})| - (\mu_x - \mu_y)}{S_p\sqrt{\frac{1}{n_x} + \frac{1}{n_y}}}$$

$\mu_x - \mu_y = 0$ from hypothesis.

9 Always state whether you accept or reject H_0 and draw a conclusion (in context if possible).

Example 13

A random sample of the heights, in centimetres, of sixth form boys and girls was taken with the following results:

Boy's heights 152, 148, 147, 157, 158, 140, 141, 144
Girl's heights 142, 146, 132, 125, 138, 131, 143

a Carry out a two-sample t-test at the 5% significance level on these data to see whether the mean height of boys exceeds the mean height of girls by 4 cm.

b State any assumptions that you have made.

Let x be the height of a boy and y be the height of a girl.

a $H_0: \mu_x = \mu_y + 4 \qquad H_1: \mu_x > \mu_y + 4$

Significance level = 0.05 (one-tailed test)

$\nu = 8 + 7 - 2 = 13$

Critical value $t_{13}(5\%) = 1.771$

The critical region is $t \geqslant 1.771$

Using a calculator gives,

for the boys $\bar{x} = 148.375$, $S_x^2 = 46.554$, $n_x = 8$

for the girls $\bar{y} = 136.714$, $S_y^2 = 57.905$, $n_y = 7$

$$S_p = \frac{(7 \times 46.554) + (6 \times 57.905)}{8 + 7 - 2}$$

$$= 51.793$$

So $S_p = 7.197$

$$t = \frac{(148.375 - 136.714) - 4}{7.197\sqrt{\frac{1}{8} + \frac{1}{7}}}$$

$$= 2.057$$

2.057 is in the critical region and so there is sufficient evidence to reject the null hypothesis. The mean height of boys exceeds the mean height of girls by 4 cm.

b The assumptions made are that the two samples are independent, that the variances of both populations are equal and that the populations are normally distributed.

1 State your hypotheses.

2 Write down the significance level. We are only interested in whether the boys are greater than the girls so it is a one-tailed test.

3 Find the number of degrees of freedom ($n_1 + n_2 - 2$ in this case).

4 Look up the critical value in the table.

5 Write down the critical region.

6 Calculate $\bar{x}$, $\bar{y}$, S_x^2 and S_y^2.

7 Calculate a pooled estimate of the variance using

$$\frac{(n_x - 1)S_x^2 + (n_y - 1)S_y^2}{n_x + n_y - 2}$$

8 Calculate t using

$$\frac{|(\bar{x} - \bar{y})| - (\mu_x - \mu_y)}{S_p\sqrt{\frac{1}{n_x} + \frac{1}{n_y}}}$$

$\mu_x - \mu_y = +4$ from hypothesis.

Always state whether you accept or reject H_0 and draw a conclusion (in context if possible).

Exercise 3D

1 A random sample of size 20 from a normal population gave $\bar{x} = 16$, $s^2 = 12$

A second random sample of size 11 from a normal population gave $\bar{x} = 14$, $s^2 = 12$

a Assuming that the both populations have the same variance, find an unbiased estimate for that variance.

b Test, at the 5% level of significance, the suggestion that the two populations have the same mean.

2 Salmon reared in Scottish fish farms are generally larger than wild salmon. A fisherman measured the length of the first 6 salmon caught on his boat at a fish farm. Their lengths in centimetres were

42.8, 40.0, 38.2, 37.5, 37.0, 36.5

Chefs prefer wild salmon to fish-farmed salmon because of their better flavour. A chef was offered 4 salmon that were claimed to be wild. Their lengths in centimetres were

42.0, 43.0, 41.5, 40.0

[illegible]e information given above and a suitable t-test at the 5% level of significance to help [illegible] to decide if the claim is likely to be correct. You may assume that the populations [illegible]nally distributed.

3 In order to check the effectiveness of three drugs against the E. *coli* bacillus, 15 cultures of the bacillus (5 for each of 3 different antibiotics) had discs soaked in the antibiotics placed in their centre. The 15 cultures were left for a time and the area in cm^2 per microgram of drug where the E. *coli* was killed was measured. The results for three different drugs are given below:

Streptomycin	0.210, 0.252, 0.251, 0.210, 0.256, 0.253
Tetracycline	0.123, 0.090, 0.123, 0.141, 0.142, 0.092
Erythromycin	0.134, 0.120, 0.123, 0.210, 0.134, 0.134

a It was thought that Tetracycline and Erythromycin seemed equally as effective. Assuming that the populations are normally distributed, test this at the 5% significance level.

b Streptomycin was thought to be more effective than either of the others. Treating the other 2 as being a single sample of 12, test this assertion at the same level of significance.

4 To test whether a new version of a computer programming language enabled faster task completion, the same task was performed by 16 programmers, divided at random into two groups. The first group used the new version of the language, and the time for task completion, in hours, for each programmer was as follows:

4.9 6.3 9.6 5.2 4.1 7.2 4.0

The second group used the old version, and their times were summarised as follows:

$$n = 9, \sum x = 71.2, \sum x^2 = 604.92$$

a State the null and alternative hypotheses.

b Perform an appropriate test at the 5% level of significance.

In order to compare like with like, experiments such as this are often performed using the same individuals in the first and the second groups.

c Give a reason why this strategy would not be appropriate in this case. **E**

5 A company undertakes investigations to compare the fuel consumption, x, in miles per gallon, of two different cars, the Volcera and the Spintono, with a view to purchasing a number as company cars.

For a random sample of 12 Volceras the fuel consumption is summarised by

$$\sum V = 384 \text{ and } \sum V^2 = 12\,480$$

A statistician incorrectly combines the figures for the sample of 12 Volceras with those of a random sample of 15 Spintonos, then carries out calculations as if they are all one larger sample and obtains the results $\bar{y} = 34$ and $s^2 = 23$

a Show that, for the sample of 15 Spintonos, $\sum x = 534$ and $\sum x^2 = 19\,330$

Given that the variance of the fuel consumption for each make of car is σ^2

b obtain an unbiased estimate for σ^2.

c Test, at the 5% level of significance, whether there is a difference between the mean fuel consumption of the two models of car. State your hypotheses and conclusion clearly.

d State any further assumption you made in order to be able to carry out your test in **c**.

e Give two precautions which could be taken when undertaking an investigation into the fuel consumption of two models of car to ensure that a fair comparison is made. **E**

3.7 You need to be able to carry out the paired *t*-test.

There are many occasions when you might want to compare results before and after some treatment, or the efficiency of two different types of treatment. You could, for example, be investigating the effect of alcohol on people's reactions, or the difference in intelligence levels of identical twins who were separated at birth and who have been brought up in different family circumstances.

In both cases you need to have a common link between the two sets of results, for instance by taking the same person's result before and after drinking alcohol, or by the twins being identical. It is necessary to have this link so that differences caused by other factors are eliminated as much as possible. It would, for example, be of little use if you tested one person's reactions without drinking alcohol and a different person's reactions after drinking alcohol because any difference could be due to normal variations between their reactions. In the same way you would have to use identical twins in the intelligence experiment, otherwise any difference in intelligence might be due to the normal variance of intelligence between different people. In these cases each result in one of the samples is paired with a result in the other sample; the results are therefore referred to as **paired**.

In paired experiments such as these you are not really interested in the individual results as such, but in the difference, D, between the results. In these circumstances you can treat the differences between pairs of matched subjects as if they were a random sample from a $N(\mu, \sigma^2)$ distribution. You can then proceed as you did for a single sample.

In book S3 you saw that if n observations are taken from a $N(\mu, \sigma^2)$ distribution, the sample mean will follow a $N\left(\mu, \frac{\sigma^2}{n}\right)$ distribution.

If you take as a null hypothesis that there is no difference between the results, then you would expect the mean of the differences $\bar{D}$ to be zero, that is to say $\bar{D}$ will then follow a $N\left(0, \frac{\sigma^2}{n}\right)$ distribution under H_0.

Note that although you do not need to assume that the two populations are normal you need to assume that that the differences are normally distributed, or if you knew σ^2 (which is very unlikely) the Central Limit Theorem would be sufficient.

If you do not know the value of σ^2 you will have to use S^2, and then as you saw from Section 2.2,

$$t = \frac{(\bar{D} - \mu_D)}{\frac{S}{\sqrt{n}}} \sim t_{n-1}$$

Taking H_0: $\mu_D = 0$ as your null hypothesis this reduces to

$$t = \frac{\bar{D} - 0}{\frac{S}{\sqrt{n}}} \sim t_{n-1}$$

■ **In a paired experiment with a mean of the differences between the samples of $\bar{D}$**

$$\frac{\bar{D} - \mu_D}{\frac{S}{\sqrt{n}}} \sim t_{n-1}$$

The paired t-test proceeds in almost the same way as the t-test itself. The steps are written below.

1 Write down the null hypothesis H_0.

2 Write down the alternative hypothesis H_1.

3 Specify α.

4 Write down the degrees of freedom (remembering that $\nu = n - 1$).

5 Write down the critical region.

6 Calculate the differences d.
Calculate $\bar{d}$ and s^2.
Calculate the value of the test statistic $t = \dfrac{(\bar{d} - \mu_D)}{\frac{s}{\sqrt{n}}}$

7 Complete the test and state your conclusions. As before the following points should be addressed:
i is the result significant or not?
ii what are the implications in terms of the original problem?

Example 14

In an experiment to test the effects of alcohol on the reaction times of people, a group of 10 students took part in an experiment. The students were asked to react to a light going on by pushing a switch that would switch it off again. Their reaction times were automatically recorded. After the students had drunk one pint of beer the experiment was repeated. The results are shown below.

Student	A	B	C	D	E	F	G	H	I	J
Reaction time before (seconds)	0.8	0.2	0.4	0.6	0.4	0.6	0.4	0.8	1.0	0.9
Reaction time after (seconds)	0.7	0.5	0.6	0.8	0.8	0.6	0.7	0.9	1.0	0.7
Difference	−0.1	0.3	0.2	0.2	0.4	0	0.3	0.1	0	−0.2

Test at the 5% significance level whether or not the consumption of a pint of beer increased the students' reaction times.

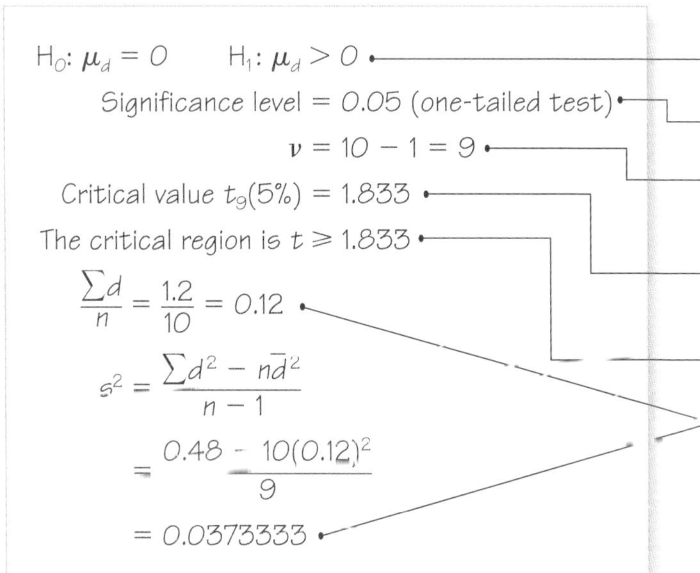

1 State your hypotheses.

2 Write down the significance level.

3 Find the number of degrees of freedom ($n - 1$ in this case).

4 Look up the critical value in the table.

5 Write down the critical region.

6 Calculate $\bar{d}$ and s^2.

$$t = \frac{0.12 - 0}{\frac{\sqrt{0.0373333}}{\sqrt{10}}} = 1.9640$$

7 Calculate the value of the test statistic $t = \frac{\bar{d} - \mu_D}{\frac{s}{\sqrt{n}}}$

1.9640 > 1.833. The result is significant: reject H_0. There is evidence that a pint of beer increases student reaction times.

Always state whether you accept or reject H_0 and draw a conclusion (in context if possible).

Example 15

In order to compare two methods of measuring the hardness of metals, readings of Brinell hardness were taken using each method for 8 different metal specimens. The resulting Brinell hardness readings are given in the table below:

Material	Reading method A	Reading method B
Aluminium	29	31
Magnesium alloy	64	63
Wrought iron	104	105
Duralumin	116	119
Mild steel	138	140
70/30 brass	156	156
Cast iron	199	200
Nickel chrome steel	385	386

Use a paired *t*-test, at the 5% level of significance, to test whether or not there is a difference in the readings given by the two methods.

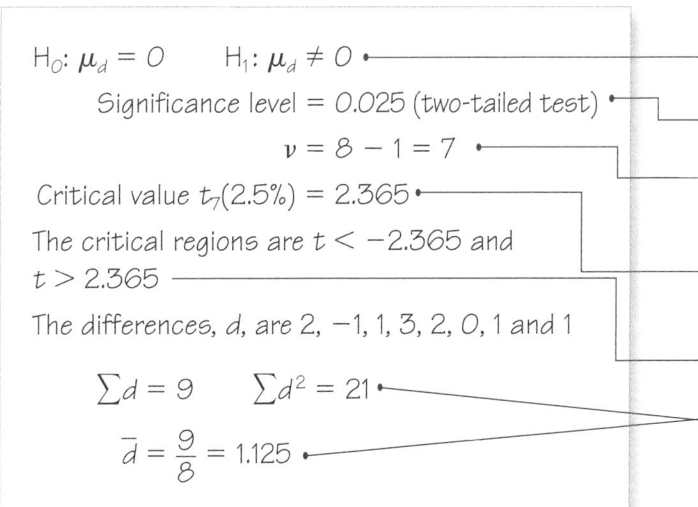

$H_0: \mu_d = 0 \quad H_1: \mu_d \neq 0$

Significance level = 0.025 (two-tailed test)

$\nu = 8 - 1 = 7$

Critical value $t_7(2.5\%) = 2.365$

The critical regions are $t < -2.365$ and $t > 2.365$

The differences, d, are 2, −1, 1, 3, 2, 0, 1 and 1

$\sum d = 9 \quad \sum d^2 = 21$

$\bar{d} = \frac{9}{8} = 1.125$

1 State your hypotheses.

2 Write down the significance level.

3 Find the number of degrees of freedom ($n - 1$ in this case).

4 Look up the critical value in the table.

5 Write down the critical region.

6 Calculate d, $\bar{d}$.

$$s^2 = \frac{\sum d^2 - n\bar{d}^2}{n-1}$$

$$= \frac{21 - 8(1.125)^2}{7}$$

$$= 1.554$$

7 Calculate s^2.

$$t = \frac{1.125 - 0}{\frac{\sqrt{1.554}}{\sqrt{8}}}$$

$$= 2.553$$

8 Calculate the value of the test statistic $t = \frac{\bar{d} - \mu_D}{\frac{s}{\sqrt{n}}}$

The t value is significant; there is sufficient evidence to reject the null hypothesis. There is a difference between the mean hardness readings using the two methods.

Always state whether you accept or reject H_0 and draw a conclusion (in context if possible).

Exercise 3E

1 It is claimed that completion of a shorthand course has increased the shorthand speeds of the students.

a If the suggestion that the mean speed of the students has not altered is to be tested, write down suitable hypotheses for which **i** a two-tailed test is appropriate, and **ii** a one-tailed test is appropriate.

The table below gives the shorthand speeds of students before and after the course.

Student	A	B	C	D	E	F
Speed before in words /minute	35	40	28	45	30	32
Speed after	42	45	28	45	40	40

b Carry out a paired t-test, at the 5% significance level, to determine whether or not there has been an increase in shorthand speeds.

2 A large number of students took two General Studies papers that were supposed to be of equal difficulty. The results for 10 students chosen at random are shown below:

Candidate	A	B	C	D	E	F	G	H	I	J
Paper 1	18	25	40	10	38	20	25	35	18	43
Paper 2	20	27	39	12	40	23	20	35	20	41

The teacher looked at the marks of a random sample of 10 students, and decided that paper 2 was easier than paper 1.

Given that the marks on each paper are normally distributed, carry out an appropriate test, at the 1% level of significance.

3 It is claimed by the manufacturer that by chewing a special flavoured chewing gum smokers are able to reduce their craving for cigarettes, and thus cut down on the number of cigarettes smoked per day. In a trial of the gum on a random selection of 10 people the no-gum smoking rate and the smoking rate when chewing the gum were investigated, with the following results:

Person	A	B	C	D	E	F	G	H	I	J
Without gum smoking rate cigs./day	20	35	40	32	45	15	22	30	34	40
With gum smoking rate cigs./day	15	25	35	30	45	15	14	25	28	34

a Use a paired *t*-test at the 5% significance level to test the manufacturer's claim.

b State any assumptions you have had to make.

4 The council of Somewhere town are going to put a new traffic management scheme into operation in the hope that it will make travel to work in the mornings quicker for most people. Before the scheme is put into operation, 10 randomly selected workers are asked to record the time it takes them to come into work on a Wednesday morning. After the scheme is put into place, the same 10 workers are again asked to record the time it takes them to come into work on a particular Wednesday morning.

The times in minutes are shown in the table below:

Worker	A	B	C	D	E	F	G	H	I	J
Before	23	37	53	42	39	60	54	85	46	38
After	18	35	49	42	34	48	52	79	37	37

Test, at the 5% significance level, whether or not the journey time to work has decreased

5 A teacher is anxious to test the idea that students' results in mock examinations are good predictors for their results in actual examinations. He selects 8 students at random from those doing a mock Statistics examination and records their marks out of 100; later he collects the same students' marks in the actual examination. The resulting marks are as follows:

Student	A	B	C	D	E	F	G	H
Mock examination mark	35	86	70	91	45	64	78	38
Actual examination	45	77	81	86	53	71	68	46

a Use a paired *t*-test to investigate whether or not the mock examination is a good predictor. (Use a 10% significance level.)

b State any assumptions you have made.

6 The manager of a dress-making company took a random sample of 10 of his employees and recorded the number of dresses made by each. He discovered that the number of dresses made between 3.00 and 5.00 p.m. was fewer than the same employees achieved between 9.00 and 11.00 a.m. He wondered if a tea break from 2.45–3.00 p.m. would increase productivity during these last two hours of the day.

The number of dresses made by these workers in the last two hours of the day before and after the introduction of the tea break were as shown below.

Worker	A	B	C	D	E	F	G	H	I	J
Before	75	73	75	81	74	73	77	75	75	72
After	80	84	79	84	85	84	78	78	80	83

a Why was the comparison made for the same ten workers?

b Conduct, at the 5% level of significance, a paired *t*-test to see if the introduction of a tea break has increased production between 3.00 and 5.00 p.m.

7 A drug administered in tablet form to help people sleep and a placebo was given for two weeks to a random sample of eight patients in a clinic. The drug and the placebo were given in random order for one week each. The average numbers of hours sleep that each patient had per night with the drug and with the placebo are given in the table below.

Patient	1	2	3	4	5	6	7	8
Hours of sleep with drug	10.5	6.7	8.9	6.7	9.2	10.9	11.9	7.6
Hours of sleep with placebo	10.3	6.5	9.0	5.3	8.7	7.5	9.3	7.2

Test, at the 1% level of significance, whether or not the drug increases the mean number of hours sleep per night. State your hypotheses clearly. E

Mixed exercise 3F

1 The random variable X has an F-distribution with 5 and 10 degrees of freedom.

Find values of a and b such that $\mathrm{P}(a \leqslant X \leqslant b) = 0.90$ E

2 A chemist has developed a fuel additive and claims that it reduces the fuel consumption of cars. To test this claim, 8 randomly selected cars were each filled with 20 litres of fuel and driven around a race circuit. Each car was tested twice, once with the additive and once without. The distances, in miles, that each car travelled before running out of fuel are given in the table below.

Car	1	2	3	4	5	6	7	8
Distance without additive	163	172	195	170	183	185	161	176
Distance with additive	168	185	187	172	180	189	172	175

Assuming that the distances travelled follow a normal distribution and stating your hypotheses clearly test, at the 10% level of significance, whether or not there is evidence to support the chemist's claim. E

3 The standard deviation of the length of a random sample of 8 fence posts produced by a timber yard was 8 mm. A second timber yard produced a random sample of 13 fence posts with a standard deviation of 14 mm.

a Test, at the 10% significance level, whether or not there is evidence that the lengths of fence posts produced by these timber yards differ in variability. State your hypotheses clearly.

b State an assumption you have made in order to carry out the test in part **a**.

4 A farmer set up a trial to assess the effect of two different diets on the increase in the weight of his lambs. He randomly selected 20 lambs. Ten of the lambs were given diet A and the other 10 lambs were given diet B. The gain in weight, in kg, of each lamb over the period of the trial was recorded.

a State why a paired t-test is not suitable for use with these data.

b Suggest an alternative method for selecting the sample which would make the use of a paired t-test valid.

c Suggest two other factors that the farmer might consider when selecting the sample.

The following paired data were collected.

Diet A	5	6	7	4.6	6.1	5.7	6.2	7.4	5	3
Diet B	7	7.2	8	6.4	5.1	7.9	8.2	6.2	6.1	5.8

d Using a paired t-test at the 5% significance level, test whether or not there is evidence of a difference in the weight gained by the lambs using diet A compared with those using diet B.

e State, giving a reason, which diet you would recommend the farmer to use for his lambs.

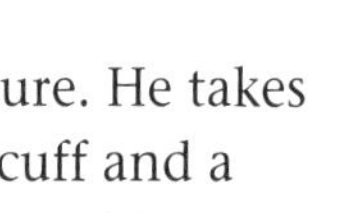

5 A medical student is investigating two methods of taking a person's blood pressure. He takes a random sample of 10 people and measures their blood pressure using an arm cuff and a finger monitor. The table below shows the blood pressure for each person, measured by each method.

Person	A	B	C	D	E	F	G	H	I	J
Arm cuff	140	110	138	127	142	112	122	128	132	160
Finger monitor	154	112	156	152	142	104	126	132	144	180

a Use a paired t-test to determine, at the 10% level of significance, whether or not there is a difference in the mean blood pressure measured using the two methods. State your hypotheses clearly.

b State an assumption about the underlying distribution of measured blood pressure required for this test.

6 The lengths, x mm, of the forewings of a random sample of male and female adult butterflies are measured. The following statistics are obtained from the data.

	Number of butterflies	Sample mean $\bar{x}$	$\sum x^2$
Females	7	50.6	17 956.5
Males	10	53.2	28 335.1

a Assuming the lengths of the forewings are normally distributed, test, at the 10% level of significance, whether or not the variances of the two distributions are the same. State your hypotheses clearly.

b Stating your hypotheses clearly test, at the 5% level of significance, whether the mean length of the forewings of the female butterflies is less than the mean length of the forewings of the male butterflies.

7 The weights, in grams, of mice are normally distributed. A biologist takes a random sample of 10 mice. She weighs each mouse and records its weight.

The ten mice are then fed on a special diet. They are weighed again after two weeks.

Their weights in grams are as follows:

Mouse	A	B	C	D	E	F	G	H	I	J
Weight before diet	50.0	48.3	47.5	54.0	38.9	42.7	50.1	46.8	40.3	41.2
Weight after diet	52.1	47.6	50.1	52.3	42.2	44.3	51.8	48.0	41.9	43.6

Stating your hypotheses clearly, and using a 1% level of significance, test whether or not the diet causes an increase in the mean weight of the mice. 

8 A hospital department installed a new, more sophisticated piece of equipment to replace an ageing one in the hope that it would speed up the treatment of patients. The treatment times of random samples of patients during the last week of operation of the old equipment and during the first week of operation of the new equipment were recorded. The summary results, in minutes, were:

	n	$\sum x$	$\sum x^2$
Old equipment	10	225	5136.3
New equipment	9	234	6200.0

a Show that the values of s^2 for the old and new equipment are 8.2 and 14.5 respectively.

Stating clearly your hypotheses, test

b whether the variance of the times using the new equipment is greater than the variance of the times using the old equipment, using a 5% significance level,

c whether there is a difference between the mean times for treatment using the new equipment and old equipment, using a 2% significance level.

d Find 95% confidence limits for the mean difference in treatment times between the new and old equipment.

Even if the new equipment would eventually lead to a reduction in treatment times, it might be that to begin with treatment times using the new equipment would be higher than those using the old equipment.

e Give one reason why this might be so.

f Suggest how the comparison between the old and new equipment could be improved. 

Summary of key points

1 For a random sample of size n_x observations from $N(\mu_x, \sigma_x^2)$ and an independent random sample of size n_y observations from $N(\mu_y, \sigma_y^2)$

$$\frac{\dfrac{S_x^2}{\sigma_x^2}}{\dfrac{S_y^2}{\sigma_y^2}} \sim F_{n_x - 1, n_y - 1}$$

2 $F_{\nu_2, \nu_1} = \dfrac{1}{F_{\nu_1, \nu_2}}$

3 If a random sample of n_x observations is taken from a normal distribution with unknown variance σ^2 and an independent sample of n_y observations is taken from a normal distribution that also has unknown variance σ^2, then a pooled estimate for σ^2 is

$$S_p^2 = \frac{(n_x - 1)S_x^2 + (n_y - 1)S_y^2}{n_x + n_y - 2}$$

4 The 95% confidence interval for the difference between two means from independent normal distributions X and Y that have equal but unknown variances is

$$\left((\bar{x} - \bar{y}) - t_{n_x + n_y - 2}(0.025) \times s_p\sqrt{\frac{1}{n_x} + \frac{1}{n_y}},\ (\bar{x} - \bar{y}) + t_{n_x + n_y - 2}(0.025) \times s_p\sqrt{\frac{1}{n_x} + \frac{1}{n_y}}\right)$$

The 90% confidence interval for the difference between two means from independent normal distributions X and Y that have equal but unknown variances is

$$\left((\bar{x} - \bar{y}) - t_{n_x + n_y - 2}(0.05) \times s_p\sqrt{\frac{1}{n_x} + \frac{1}{n_y}},\ (\bar{x} - \bar{y}) + t_{n_x + n_y - 2}(0.05) \times s_p\sqrt{\frac{1}{n_x} + \frac{1}{n_y}}\right)$$

5 If a random sample of n_x observations is taken from a normal distribution that has an unknown variance σ^2 and an independent sample of n_y observations is taken from a normal distribution with equal variance, then

$$\frac{\bar{X} - \bar{Y} - (\mu_x - \mu_y)}{S_p\sqrt{\dfrac{1}{n_x} + \dfrac{1}{n_y}}} \sim t_{n_x + n_y - 2}$$

6 In a paired experiment with the mean of the difference between the samples of D

$$\frac{\bar{D} - \mu_D}{\dfrac{S}{\sqrt{n}}} \sim t_{n - 1}$$

2 Review Exercise

1 The random variable X has an F distribution with 10 and 12 degrees of freedom. Find a and b such that $P(a < X < b) = 0.90$ *E*

2 A doctor believes that the span of a person's dominant hand is greater than that of the weaker hand. To test this theory, the doctor measures the spans of the dominant and weaker hands of a random sample of 8 people. He subtracts the span of the weaker hand from that of the dominant hand. The spans, in millimetres, are summarised in the table below.

	Dominant hand	Weaker hand
A	202	195
B	251	249
C	215	218
D	235	234
E	210	211
F	195	197
G	191	181
H	230	225

Test, at the 5% significance level, the doctor's belief. *E*

3 The times, x seconds, taken by the competitors in the 100 m freestyle events at a school swimming gala are recorded. The following statistics are obtained from the data.

	Number of competitors	Sample mean $\bar{x}$	$\sum x^2$
Girls	8	83.10	55 746
Boys	7	88.90	56 130

Following the gala a proud parent claims that girls are faster swimmers than boys. Assuming that the times taken by the competitors are two independent random samples from normal distributions,

a test, at the 10% level of significance, whether or not the variances of the two distributions are the same. State your hypotheses clearly.

b Stating your hypotheses clearly, test the parent's claim. Use a 5% level of significance. *E*

4 Two methods of extracting juice from an orange are to be compared. Eight oranges are halved. One half of each orange is chosen at random and allocated to

Examination style paper

1 [In this question you may assume that the random variable Y with a χ_ν^2 distribution has $\mathrm{E}(Y) = \nu$ and $\mathrm{Var}(Y) = 2\nu$.]

A random sample of size n is taken from a normal population with variance σ^2.

Show that the statistic S^2 is a consistent estimator of σ^2.

(6 marks)

2 The weights, in grams, of apples are assumed to follow a normal distribution.

The weights of apples sold by a supermarket have variance σ_s^2.

A random sample of 5 apples from a supermarket had weights, in grams, of

115, 110, 118, 124, 109

The weights of apples sold on a market stall have variance σ_m^2.

An independent random sample of 6 apples from a market stall had sample variance $s_m^2 = 240.3$

Stating your hypotheses clearly test, at the 5% level of significance, whether or not there is evidence that $\sigma_m^2 > \sigma_s^2$.

(7 marks)

3 A drive in tyre-replacement company requires its mechanics to change tyres. The time, T minutes, to change a tyre is believed to follow a normal distribution with variance 11.16 and new recruits are expected to maintain this variance. A random sample of 12 times are recorded for a new recruit and the sample variance s_T^2 is calculated.

a Stating your hypotheses clearly find the critical region for s_T^2 to determine whether or not the variance of times for the new recruit is more than 11.16. Use a 1% level of significance and give your answer to 3 decimal places. (4)

Given that the actual value of σ_T^2 for the new recruit is 49.45

b calculate P(Type II error) using this test. (3)

(7 marks)

4 The manufacturers of a fuel additive claim it reduces the fuel consumption of cars. To test this claim a random sample of 7 cars were each filled with 5 litres of fuel and driven around a test track. Each car was tested twice: once with the fuel additive and once without. The distances, in miles, that each car travelled before running out of fuel are given in the following table.

Car	1	2	3	4	5	6	7
Distance without additive	41	50	63	53	48	62	54
Distance with additive	44	49	65	59	43	67	60

a Stating your hypotheses clearly test, at the 10% level of significance, whether or not there is evidence to support the manufacturer's claim. (8)

b State an assumption you have made to carry out the test in part **a**. (1)

(Total 9 marks)

5 A horticulturalist is testing the effect of playing music on tomato seedlings. Two independent random samples of seedlings are selected and their height gained over a 30 day period is recorded. One sample of 10 seedlings are regularly played some soothing classical music whilst the other sample of 13 seedlings are placed in an identical environment but without the music. The heights gained (x cm) by both sets of seedlings are summarised by the statistics in the table below.

	Sample size	Mean $\bar{x}$	Standard deviation s
With music	10	23.36	5.29
Without music	13	19.96	6.84

a Use a two-tailed test to show that, at the 10% level of significance, the variances of the heights gained by the seedlings with and without music can be assumed to be equal. State your hypotheses clearly. (4)

b Stating your hypotheses clearly test, at the 5% level of significance, whether or not there is a difference in the mean height gained by the two groups of seedlings. (7)

c State the importance of the test in **a** to your test in part **b**. (1)

(12 marks)

6 A doctor believes that the span of an adult male's hand, in mm, is normally distributed with a mean of μ mm and a standard deviation of σ mm. A random sample of 6 men's hands were measured and the results are given below

202, 218, 220, 215, 225, 209

a Find a 95% confidence interval for

i μ, **ii** σ. (11)

b Use appropriate confidence limits from **a** to find, to 2 decimal places, the highest estimate of the proportion of adult males with a hand span greater than 230 mm. (4)

(15 marks)

7 A cube C has sides of length t and volume t^3. A point P with coordinates (X, Y, Z) is selected at random from inside the cube and the coordinates are used to estimate t^3. It is assumed that X, Y and Z are independent random variables each having a continuous uniform distribution over $[0, t]$.

a Use integration to show that $\text{E}(X^n) = \dfrac{t^n}{n+1}$ (3)

b Show that $U = X^3 + Y^3 + Z^3$ is a biased estimator of t^3 and find the bias. (4)

c Show that $S = 2X^3 + Y^3 + Z^3$ is an unbiased estimator of t^3. (2)

d Find Var(S). (4)

An alternative estimator $T = k(X^3 + Y^3 + Z^3)$, where k is a constant, is proposed as an unbiased estimator of t^3.

e Find the value of the constant k. (2)

f Find Var(T). (2)

g State, giving a reason, which of S and T is the better estimator of t^3. (1)

The point (1, 3, 2) is selected from inside C.

h Using your estimator chosen in **g** find an estimate for the volume of C. (1)

(19 marks)

Appendix

THE NORMAL DISTRIBUTION FUNCTION

The function tabulated below is $\Phi(z)$, defined as $\Phi(z) = \dfrac{1}{\sqrt{2\pi}} \displaystyle\int_{-\infty}^{z} e^{-\frac{1}{2}t^2}\, dt$.

z	$P(Z<z)$	z	$P(Z<z)$	z	$P(Z<z)$	z	$P(Z<z)$	z	$P(Z<z)$
0.00	0.5000	0.50	0.6915	1.00	0.8413	1.50	0.9332	2.00	0.9772
0.01	0.5040	0.51	0.6950	1.01	0.8438	1.51	0.9345	2.02	0.9783
0.02	0.5080	0.52	0.6985	1.02	0.8461	1.52	0.9357	2.04	0.9793
0.03	0.5120	0.53	0.7019	1.03	0.8485	1.53	0.9370	2.06	0.9803
0.04	0.5160	0.54	0.7054	1.04	0.8508	1.54	0.9382	2.08	0.9812
0.05	0.5199	0.55	0.7088	1.05	0.8531	1.55	0.9394	2.10	0.9821
0.06	0.5239	0.56	0.7123	1.06	0.8554	1.56	0.9406	2.12	0.9830
0.07	0.5279	0.57	0.7157	1.07	0.8577	1.57	0.9418	2.14	0.9838
0.08	0.5319	0.58	0.7190	1.08	0.8599	1.58	0.9429	2.16	0.9846
0.09	0.5359	0.59	0.7224	1.09	0.8621	1.59	0.9441	2.18	0.9854
0.10	0.5398	0.60	0.7257	1.10	0.8643	1.60	0.9452	2.20	0.9861
0.11	0.5438	0.61	0.7291	1.11	0.8665	1.61	0.9463	2.22	0.9868
0.12	0.5478	0.62	0.7324	1.12	0.8686	1.62	0.9474	2.24	0.9875
0.13	0.5517	0.63	0.7357	1.13	0.8708	1.63	0.9484	2.26	0.9881
0.14	0.5557	0.64	0.7389	1.14	0.8729	1.64	0.9495	2.28	0.9887
0.15	0.5596	0.65	0.7422	1.15	0.8749	1.65	0.9505	2.30	0.9893
0.16	0.5636	0.66	0.7454	1.16	0.8770	1.66	0.9515	2.32	0.9898
0.17	0.5675	0.67	0.7486	1.17	0.8790	1.67	0.9525	2.34	0.9904
0.18	0.5714	0.68	0.7517	1.18	0.8810	1.68	0.9535	2.36	0.9909
0.19	0.5753	0.69	0.7549	1.19	0.8830	1.69	0.9545	2.38	0.9913
0.20	0.5793	0.70	0.7580	1.20	0.8849	1.70	0.9554	2.40	0.9918
0.21	0.5832	0.71	0.7611	1.21	0.8869	1.71	0.9564	2.42	0.9922
0.22	0.5871	0.72	0.7642	1.22	0.8888	1.72	0.9573	2.44	0.9927
0.23	0.5910	0.73	0.7673	1.23	0.8907	1.73	0.9582	2.46	0.9931
0.24	0.5948	0.74	0.7704	1.24	0.8925	1.74	0.9591	2.48	0.9934
0.25	0.5987	0.75	0.7734	1.25	0.8944	1.75	0.9599	2.50	0.9938
0.26	0.6026	0.76	0.7764	1.26	0.8962	1.76	0.9608	2.55	0.9946
0.27	0.6064	0.77	0.7794	1.27	0.8980	1.77	0.9616	2.60	0.9953
0.28	0.6103	0.78	0.7823	1.28	0.8997	1.78	0.9625	2.65	0.9960
0.29	0.6141	0.79	0.7852	1.29	0.9015	1.79	0.9633	2.70	0.9965
0.30	0.6179	0.80	0.7881	1.30	0.9032	1.80	0.9641	2.75	0.9970
0.31	0.6217	0.81	0.7910	1.31	0.9049	1.81	0.9649	2.80	0.9974
0.32	0.6255	0.82	0.7939	1.32	0.9066	1.82	0.9656	2.85	0.9978
0.33	0.6293	0.83	0.7967	1.33	0.9082	1.83	0.9664	2.90	0.9981
0.34	0.6331	0.84	0.7995	1.34	0.9099	1.84	0.9671	2.95	0.9984
0.35	0.6368	0.85	0.8023	1.35	0.9115	1.85	0.9678	3.00	0.9987
0.36	0.6406	0.86	0.8051	1.36	0.9131	1.86	0.9686	3.05	0.9989
0.37	0.6443	0.87	0.8078	1.37	0.9147	1.87	0.9693	3.10	0.9990
0.38	0.6480	0.88	0.8106	1.38	0.9162	1.88	0.9699	3.15	0.9992
0.39	0.6517	0.89	0.8133	1.39	0.9177	1.89	0.9706	3.20	0.9993
0.40	0.6554	0.90	0.8159	1.40	0.9192	1.90	0.9713	3.25	0.9994
0.41	0.6591	0.91	0.8186	1.41	0.9207	1.91	0.9719	3.30	0.9995
0.42	0.6628	0.92	0.8212	1.42	0.9222	1.92	0.9726	3.35	0.9996
0.43	0.6664	0.93	0.8238	1.43	0.9236	1.93	0.9732	3.40	0.9997
0.44	0.6700	0.94	0.8264	1.44	0.9251	1.94	0.9738	3.50	0.9998
0.45	0.6736	0.95	0.8289	1.45	0.9265	1.95	0.9744	3.60	0.9998
0.46	0.6772	0.96	0.8315	1.46	0.9279	1.96	0.9750	3.70	0.9999
0.47	0.6808	0.97	0.8340	1.47	0.9292	1.97	0.9756	3.80	0.9999
0.48	0.6844	0.98	0.8365	1.48	0.9306	1.98	0.9761	3.90	1.0000
0.49	0.6879	0.99	0.8389	1.49	0.9319	1.99	0.9767	4.00	1.0000
0.50	0.6915	1.00	0.8413	1.50	0.9332	2.00	0.9772		

PERCENTAGE POINTS OF THE NORMAL DISTRIBUTION

The values z in the table are those which a random variable $Z \sim N(0,1)$ exceeds with probability p; that is, $P(Z > z) = p$.

p	z	p	z
0.5000	0.0000	0.0500	1.6449
0.4000	0.2533	0.0250	1.9600
0.3000	0.5244	0.0100	2.3263
0.2000	0.8416	0.0050	2.5758
0.1500	1.0364	0.0010	3.0902
0.1000	1.2816	0.0005	3.2905

BINOMIAL CUMULATIVE DISTRIBUTION FUNCTION

The tabulated value is $P(X \leqslant x)$, where X has a binomial distribution with index n and parameter p.

$p =$	0.05	0.10	0.15	0.20	0.25	0.30	0.35	0.40	0.45	0.50
$n = 5, x = 0$	0.7738	0.5905	0.4437	0.3277	0.2373	0.1681	0.1160	0.0778	0.0503	0.0312
1	0.9774	0.9185	0.8352	0.7373	0.6328	0.5282	0.4284	0.3370	0.2562	0.1875
2	0.9988	0.9914	0.9734	0.9421	0.8965	0.8369	0.7648	0.6826	0.5931	0.5000
3	1.0000	0.9995	0.9978	0.9933	0.9844	0.9692	0.9460	0.9130	0.8688	0.8125
4	1.0000	1.0000	0.9999	0.9997	0.9990	0.9976	0.9947	0.9898	0.9815	0.9688
$n = 6, x = 0$	0.7351	0.5314	0.3771	0.2621	0.1780	0.1176	0.0754	0.0467	0.0277	0.0156
1	0.9672	0.8857	0.7765	0.6554	0.5339	0.4202	0.3191	0.2333	0.1636	0.1094
2	0.9978	0.9842	0.9527	0.9011	0.8306	0.7443	0.6471	0.5443	0.4415	0.3438
3	0.9999	0.9987	0.9941	0.9830	0.9624	0.9295	0.8826	0.8208	0.7447	0.6563
4	1.0000	0.9999	0.9996	0.9984	0.9954	0.9891	0.9777	0.9590	0.9308	0.8906
5	1.0000	1.0000	1.0000	0.9999	0.9998	0.9993	0.9982	0.9959	0.9917	0.9844
$n = 7, x = 0$	0.6983	0.4783	0.3206	0.2097	0.1335	0.0824	0.0490	0.0280	0.0152	0.0078
1	0.9556	0.8503	0.7166	0.5767	0.4449	0.3294	0.2338	0.1586	0.1024	0.0625
2	0.9962	0.9743	0.9262	0.8520	0.7564	0.6471	0.5323	0.4199	0.3164	0.2266
3	0.9998	0.9973	0.9879	0.9667	0.9294	0.8740	0.8002	0.7102	0.6083	0.5000
4	1.0000	0.9998	0.9988	0.9953	0.9871	0.9712	0.9444	0.9037	0.8471	0.7734
5	1.0000	1.0000	0.9999	0.9996	0.9987	0.9962	0.9910	0.9812	0.9643	0.9375
6	1.0000	1.0000	1.0000	1.0000	0.9999	0.9998	0.9994	0.9984	0.9963	0.9922
$n = 8, x = 0$	0.6634	0.4305	0.2725	0.1678	0.1001	0.0576	0.0319	0.0168	0.0084	0.0039
1	0.9428	0.8131	0.6572	0.5033	0.3671	0.2553	0.1691	0.1064	0.0632	0.0352
2	0.9942	0.9619	0.8948	0.7969	0.6785	0.5518	0.4278	0.3154	0.2201	0.1445
3	0.9996	0.9950	0.9786	0.9437	0.8862	0.8059	0.7064	0.5941	0.4770	0.3633
4	1.0000	0.9996	0.9971	0.9896	0.9727	0.9420	0.8939	0.8263	0.7396	0.6367
5	1.0000	1.0000	0.9998	0.9988	0.9958	0.9887	0.9747	0.9502	0.9115	0.8555
6	1.0000	1.0000	1.0000	0.9999	0.9996	0.9987	0.9964	0.9915	0.9819	0.9648
7	1.0000	1.0000	1.0000	1.0000	1.0000	0.9999	0.9998	0.9993	0.9983	0.9961
$n = 9, x = 0$	0.6302	0.3874	0.2316	0.1342	0.0751	0.0404	0.0207	0.0101	0.0046	0.0020
1	0.9288	0.7748	0.5995	0.4362	0.3003	0.1960	0.1211	0.0705	0.0385	0.0195
2	0.9916	0.9470	0.8591	0.7382	0.6007	0.4628	0.3373	0.2318	0.1495	0.0898
3	0.9994	0.9917	0.9661	0.9144	0.8343	0.7297	0.6089	0.4826	0.3614	0.2539
4	1.0000	0.9991	0.9944	0.9804	0.9511	0.9012	0.8283	0.7334	0.6214	0.5000
5	1.0000	0.9999	0.9994	0.9969	0.9900	0.9747	0.9464	0.9006	0.8342	0.7461
6	1.0000	1.0000	1.0000	0.9997	0.9987	0.9957	0.9888	0.9750	0.9502	0.9102
7	1.0000	1.0000	1.0000	1.0000	0.9999	0.9996	0.9986	0.9962	0.9909	0.9805
8	1.0000	1.0000	1.0000	1.0000	1.0000	1.0000	0.9999	0.9997	0.9992	0.9980
$n = 10, x = 0$	0.5987	0.3487	0.1969	0.1074	0.0563	0.0282	0.0135	0.0060	0.0025	0.0010
1	0.9139	0.7361	0.5443	0.3758	0.2440	0.1493	0.0860	0.0464	0.0233	0.0107
2	0.9885	0.9298	0.8202	0.6778	0.5256	0.3828	0.2616	0.1673	0.0996	0.0547
3	0.9990	0.9872	0.9500	0.8791	0.7759	0.6496	0.5138	0.3823	0.2660	0.1719
4	0.9999	0.9984	0.9901	0.9672	0.9219	0.8497	0.7515	0.6331	0.5044	0.3770
5	1.0000	0.9999	0.9986	0.9936	0.9803	0.9527	0.9051	0.8338	0.7384	0.6230
6	1.0000	1.0000	0.9999	0.9991	0.9965	0.9894	0.9740	0.9452	0.8980	0.8281
7	1.0000	1.0000	1.0000	0.9999	0.9996	0.9984	0.9952	0.9877	0.9726	0.9453
8	1.0000	1.0000	1.0000	1.0000	1.0000	0.9999	0.9995	0.9983	0.9955	0.9893
9	1.0000	1.0000	1.0000	1.0000	1.0000	1.0000	1.0000	0.9999	0.9997	0.9990

$p =$	0.05	0.10	0.15	0.20	0.25	0.30	0.35	0.40	0.45	0.50
$n = 12, x = 0$	0.5404	0.2824	0.1422	0.0687	0.0317	0.0138	0.0057	0.0022	0.0008	0.0002
1	0.8816	0.6590	0.4435	0.2749	0.1584	0.0850	0.0424	0.0196	0.0083	0.0032
2	0.9804	0.8891	0.7358	0.5583	0.3907	0.2528	0.1513	0.0834	0.0421	0.0193
3	0.9978	0.9744	0.9078	0.7946	0.6488	0.4925	0.3467	0.2253	0.1345	0.0730
4	0.9998	0.9957	0.9761	0.9274	0.8424	0.7237	0.5833	0.4382	0.3044	0.1938
5	1.0000	0.9995	0.9954	0.9806	0.9456	0.8822	0.7873	0.6652	0.5269	0.3872
6	1.0000	0.9999	0.9993	0.9961	0.9857	0.9614	0.9154	0.8418	0.7393	0.6128
7	1.0000	1.0000	0.9999	0.9994	0.9972	0.9905	0.9745	0.9427	0.8883	0.8062
8	1.0000	1.0000	1.0000	0.9999	0.9996	0.9983	0.9944	0.9847	0.9644	0.9270
9	1.0000	1.0000	1.0000	1.0000	1.0000	0.9998	0.9992	0.9972	0.9921	0.9807
10	1.0000	1.0000	1.0000	1.0000	1.0000	1.0000	0.9999	0.9997	0.9989	0.9968
11	1.0000	1.0000	1.0000	1.0000	1.0000	1.0000	1.0000	1.0000	0.9999	0.9998
$n = 15, x = 0$	0.4633	0.2059	0.0874	0.0352	0.0134	0.0047	0.0016	0.0005	0.0001	0.0000
1	0.8290	0.5490	0.3186	0.1671	0.0802	0.0353	0.0142	0.0052	0.0017	0.0005
2	0.9638	0.8159	0.6042	0.3980	0.2361	0.1268	0.0617	0.0271	0.0107	0.0037
3	0.9945	0.9444	0.8227	0.6482	0.4613	0.2969	0.1727	0.0905	0.0424	0.0176
4	0.9994	0.9873	0.9383	0.8358	0.6865	0.5155	0.3519	0.2173	0.1204	0.0592
5	0.9999	0.9978	0.9832	0.9389	0.8516	0.7216	0.5643	0.4032	0.2608	0.1509
6	1.0000	0.9997	0.9964	0.9819	0.9434	0.8689	0.7548	0.6098	0.4522	0.3036
7	1.0000	1.0000	0.9994	0.9958	0.9827	0.9500	0.8868	0.7869	0.6535	0.5000
8	1.0000	1.0000	0.9999	0.9992	0.9958	0.9848	0.9578	0.9050	0.8182	0.6964
9	1.0000	1.0000	1.0000	0.9999	0.9992	0.9963	0.9876	0.9662	0.9231	0.8491
10	1.0000	1.0000	1.0000	1.0000	0.9999	0.9993	0.9972	0.9907	0.9745	0.9408
11	1.0000	1.0000	1.0000	1.0000	1.0000	0.9999	0.9995	0.9981	0.9937	0.9824
12	1.0000	1.0000	1.0000	1.0000	1.0000	1.0000	0.9999	0.9997	0.9989	0.9963
13	1.0000	1.0000	1.0000	1.0000	1.0000	1.0000	1.0000	1.0000	0.9999	0.9995
14	1.0000	1.0000	1.0000	1.0000	1.0000	1.0000	1.0000	1.0000	1.0000	1.0000
$n = 20, x = 0$	0.3585	0.1216	0.0388	0.0115	0.0032	0.0008	0.0002	0.0000	0.0000	0.0000
1	0.7358	0.3917	0.1756	0.0692	0.0243	0.0076	0.0021	0.0005	0.0001	0.0000
2	0.9245	0.6769	0.4049	0.2061	0.0913	0.0355	0.0121	0.0036	0.0009	0.0002
3	0.9841	0.8670	0.6477	0.4114	0.2252	0.1071	0.0444	0.0160	0.0049	0.0013
4	0.9974	0.9568	0.8298	0.6296	0.4148	0.2375	0.1182	0.0510	0.0189	0.0059
5	0.9997	0.9887	0.9327	0.8042	0.6172	0.4164	0.2454	0.1256	0.0553	0.0207
6	1.0000	0.9976	0.9781	0.9133	0.7858	0.6080	0.4166	0.2500	0.1299	0.0577
7	1.0000	0.9996	0.9941	0.9679	0.8982	0.7723	0.6010	0.4159	0.2520	0.1316
8	1.0000	0.9999	0.9987	0.9900	0.9591	0.8867	0.7624	0.5956	0.4143	0.2517
9	1.0000	1.0000	0.9998	0.9974	0.9861	0.9520	0.8782	0.7553	0.5914	0.4119
10	1.0000	1.0000	1.0000	0.9994	0.9961	0.9829	0.9468	0.8725	0.7507	0.5881
11	1.0000	1.0000	1.0000	0.9999	0.9991	0.9949	0.9804	0.9435	0.8692	0.7483
12	1.0000	1.0000	1.0000	1.0000	0.9998	0.9987	0.9940	0.9790	0.9420	0.8684
13	1.0000	1.0000	1.0000	1.0000	1.0000	0.9997	0.9985	0.9935	0.9786	0.9423
14	1.0000	1.0000	1.0000	1.0000	1.0000	1.0000	0.9997	0.9984	0.9936	0.9793
15	1.0000	1.0000	1.0000	1.0000	1.0000	1.0000	1.0000	0.9997	0.9985	0.9941
16	1.0000	1.0000	1.0000	1.0000	1.0000	1.0000	1.0000	1.0000	0.9997	0.9987
17	1.0000	1.0000	1.0000	1.0000	1.0000	1.0000	1.0000	1.0000	1.0000	0.9998
18	1.0000	1.0000	1.0000	1.0000	1.0000	1.0000	1.0000	1.0000	1.0000	1.0000

$p =$	0.05	0.10	0.15	0.20	0.25	0.30	0.35	0.40	0.45	0.50
$n = 25, x = 0$	0.2774	0.0718	0.0172	0.0038	0.0008	0.0001	0.0000	0.0000	0.0000	0.0000
1	0.6424	0.2712	0.0931	0.0274	0.0070	0.0016	0.0003	0.0001	0.0000	0.0000
2	0.8729	0.5371	0.2537	0.0982	0.0321	0.0090	0.0021	0.0004	0.0001	0.0000
3	0.9659	0.7636	0.4711	0.2340	0.0962	0.0332	0.0097	0.0024	0.0005	0.0001
4	0.9928	0.9020	0.6821	0.4207	0.2137	0.0905	0.0320	0.0095	0.0023	0.0005
5	0.9988	0.9666	0.8385	0.6167	0.3783	0.1935	0.0826	0.0294	0.0086	0.0020
6	0.9998	0.9905	0.9305	0.7800	0.5611	0.3407	0.1734	0.0736	0.0258	0.0073
7	1.0000	0.9977	0.9745	0.8909	0.7265	0.5118	0.3061	0.1536	0.0639	0.0216
8	1.0000	0.9995	0.9920	0.9532	0.8506	0.6769	0.4668	0.2735	0.1340	0.0539
9	1.0000	0.9999	0.9979	0.9827	0.9287	0.8106	0.6303	0.4246	0.2424	0.1148
10	1.0000	1.0000	0.9995	0.9944	0.9703	0.9022	0.7712	0.5858	0.3843	0.2122
11	1.0000	1.0000	0.9999	0.9985	0.9893	0.9558	0.8746	0.7323	0.5426	0.3450
12	1.0000	1.0000	1.0000	0.9996	0.9966	0.9825	0.9396	0.8462	0.6937	0.5000
13	1.0000	1.0000	1.0000	0.9999	0.9991	0.9940	0.9745	0.9222	0.8173	0.6550
14	1.0000	1.0000	1.0000	1.0000	0.9998	0.9982	0.9907	0.9656	0.9040	0.7878
15	1.0000	1.0000	1.0000	1.0000	1.0000	0.9995	0.9971	0.9868	0.9560	0.8852
16	1.0000	1.0000	1.0000	1.0000	1.0000	0.9999	0.9992	0.9957	0.9826	0.9461
17	1.0000	1.0000	1.0000	1.0000	1.0000	1.0000	0.9998	0.9988	0.9942	0.9784
18	1.0000	1.0000	1.0000	1.0000	1.0000	1.0000	1.0000	0.9997	0.9984	0.9927
19	1.0000	1.0000	1.0000	1.0000	1.0000	1.0000	1.0000	0.9999	0.9996	0.9980
20	1.0000	1.0000	1.0000	1.0000	1.0000	1.0000	1.0000	1.0000	0.9999	0.9995
21	1.0000	1.0000	1.0000	1.0000	1.0000	1.0000	1.0000	1.0000	1.0000	0.9999
22	1.0000	1.0000	1.0000	1.0000	1.0000	1.0000	1.0000	1.0000	1.0000	1.0000
$n = 30, x = 0$	0.2146	0.0424	0.0076	0.0012	0.0002	0.0000	0.0000	0.0000	0.0000	0.0000
1	0.5535	0.1837	0.0480	0.0105	0.0020	0.0003	0.0000	0.0000	0.0000	0.0000
2	0.8122	0.4114	0.1514	0.0442	0.0106	0.0021	0.0003	0.0000	0.0000	0.0000
3	0.9392	0.6474	0.3217	0.1227	0.0374	0.0093	0.0019	0.0003	0.0000	0.0000
4	0.9844	0.8245	0.5245	0.2552	0.0979	0.0302	0.0075	0.0015	0.0002	0.0000
5	0.9967	0.9268	0.7106	0.4275	0.2026	0.0766	0.0233	0.0057	0.0011	0.0002
6	0.9994	0.9742	0.8474	0.6070	0.3481	0.1595	0.0586	0.0172	0.0040	0.0007
7	0.9999	0.9922	0.9302	0.7608	0.5143	0.2814	0.1238	0.0435	0.0121	0.0026
8	1.0000	0.9980	0.9722	0.8713	0.6736	0.4315	0.2247	0.0940	0.0312	0.0081
9	1.0000	0.9995	0.9903	0.9389	0.8034	0.5888	0.3575	0.1763	0.0694	0.0214
10	1.0000	0.9999	0.9971	0.9744	0.8943	0.7304	0.5078	0.2915	0.1350	0.0494
11	1.0000	1.0000	0.9992	0.9905	0.9493	0.8407	0.6548	0.4311	0.2327	0.1002
12	1.0000	1.0000	0.9998	0.9969	0.9784	0.9155	0.7802	0.5785	0.3592	0.1808
13	1.0000	1.0000	1.0000	0.9991	0.9918	0.9599	0.8737	0.7145	0.5025	0.2923
14	1.0000	1.0000	1.0000	0.9998	0.9973	0.9831	0.9348	0.8246	0.6448	0.4278
15	1.0000	1.0000	1.0000	0.9999	0.9992	0.9936	0.9699	0.9029	0.7691	0.5722
16	1.0000	1.0000	1.0000	1.0000	0.9998	0.9979	0.9876	0.9519	0.8644	0.7077
17	1.0000	1.0000	1.0000	1.0000	0.9999	0.9994	0.9955	0.9788	0.9286	0.8192
18	1.0000	1.0000	1.0000	1.0000	1.0000	0.9998	0.9986	0.9917	0.9666	0.8998
19	1.0000	1.0000	1.0000	1.0000	1.0000	1.0000	0.9996	0.9971	0.9862	0.9506
20	1.0000	1.0000	1.0000	1.0000	1.0000	1.0000	0.9999	0.9991	0.9950	0.9786
21	1.0000	1.0000	1.0000	1.0000	1.0000	1.0000	1.0000	0.9998	0.9984	0.9919
22	1.0000	1.0000	1.0000	1.0000	1.0000	1.0000	1.0000	1.0000	0.9996	0.9971
23	1.0000	1.0000	1.0000	1.0000	1.0000	1.0000	1.0000	1.0000	0.9999	0.9993
24	1.0000	1.0000	1.0000	1.0000	1.0000	1.0000	1.0000	1.0000	1.0000	0.9998
25	1.0000	1.0000	1.0000	1.0000	1.0000	1.0000	1.0000	1.0000	1.0000	1.0000

$p =$	0.05	0.10	0.15	0.20	0.25	0.30	0.35	0.40	0.45	0.50
$n = 40, x = 0$	0.1285	0.0148	0.0015	0.0001	0.0000	0.0000	0.0000	0.0000	0.0000	0.0000
1	0.3991	0.0805	0.0121	0.0015	0.0001	0.0000	0.0000	0.0000	0.0000	0.0000
2	0.6767	0.2228	0.0486	0.0079	0.0010	0.0001	0.0000	0.0000	0.0000	0.0000
3	0.8619	0.4231	0.1302	0.0285	0.0047	0.0006	0.0001	0.0000	0.0000	0.0000
4	0.9520	0.6290	0.2633	0.0759	0.0160	0.0026	0.0003	0.0000	0.0000	0.0000
5	0.9861	0.7937	0.4325	0.1613	0.0433	0.0086	0.0013	0.0001	0.0000	0.0000
6	0.9966	0.9005	0.6067	0.2859	0.0962	0.0238	0.0044	0.0006	0.0001	0.0000
7	0.9993	0.9581	0.7559	0.4371	0.1820	0.0553	0.0124	0.0021	0.0002	0.0000
8	0.9999	0.9845	0.8646	0.5931	0.2998	0.1110	0.0303	0.0061	0.0009	0.0001
9	1.0000	0.9949	0.9328	0.7318	0.4395	0.1959	0.0644	0.0156	0.0027	0.0003
10	1.0000	0.9985	0.9701	0.8392	0.5839	0.3087	0.1215	0.0352	0.0074	0.0011
11	1.0000	0.9996	0.9880	0.9125	0.7151	0.4406	0.2053	0.0709	0.0179	0.0032
12	1.0000	0.9999	0.9957	0.9568	0.8209	0.5772	0.3143	0.1285	0.0386	0.0083
13	1.0000	1.0000	0.9986	0.9806	0.8968	0.7032	0.4408	0.2112	0.0751	0.0192
14	1.0000	1.0000	0.9996	0.9921	0.9456	0.8074	0.5721	0.3174	0.1326	0.0403
15	1.0000	1.0000	0.9999	0.9971	0.9738	0.8849	0.6946	0.4402	0.2142	0.0769
16	1.0000	1.0000	1.0000	0.9990	0.9884	0.9367	0.7978	0.5681	0.3185	0.1341
17	1.0000	1.0000	1.0000	0.9997	0.9953	0.9680	0.8761	0.6885	0.4391	0.2148
18	1.0000	1.0000	1.0000	0.9999	0.9983	0.9852	0.9301	0.7911	0.5651	0.3179
19	1.0000	1.0000	1.0000	1.0000	0.9994	0.9937	0.9637	0.8702	0.6844	0.4373
20	1.0000	1.0000	1.0000	1.0000	0.9998	0.9976	0.9827	0.9256	0.7870	0.5627
21	1.0000	1.0000	1.0000	1.0000	1.0000	0.9991	0.9925	0.9608	0.8669	0.6821
22	1.0000	1.0000	1.0000	1.0000	1.0000	0.9997	0.9970	0.9811	0.9233	0.7852
23	1.0000	1.0000	1.0000	1.0000	1.0000	0.9999	0.9989	0.9917	0.9595	0.8659
24	1.0000	1.0000	1.0000	1.0000	1.0000	1.0000	0.9996	0.9966	0.9804	0.9231
25	1.0000	1.0000	1.0000	1.0000	1.0000	1.0000	0.9999	0.9988	0.9914	0.9597
26	1.0000	1.0000	1.0000	1.0000	1.0000	1.0000	1.0000	0.9996	0.9966	0.9808
27	1.0000	1.0000	1.0000	1.0000	1.0000	1.0000	1.0000	0.9999	0.9988	0.9917
28	1.0000	1.0000	1.0000	1.0000	1.0000	1.0000	1.0000	1.0000	0.9996	0.9968
29	1.0000	1.0000	1.0000	1.0000	1.0000	1.0000	1.0000	1.0000	0.9999	0.9989
30	1.0000	1.0000	1.0000	1.0000	1.0000	1.0000	1.0000	1.0000	1.0000	0.9997
31	1.0000	1.0000	1.0000	1.0000	1.0000	1.0000	1.0000	1.0000	1.0000	0.9999
32	1.0000	1.0000	1.0000	1.0000	1.0000	1.0000	1.0000	1.0000	1.0000	1.0000

$p =$	0.05	0.10	0.15	0.20	0.25	0.30	0.35	0.40	0.45	0.50
$n = 50, x = 0$	0.0769	0.0052	0.0003	0.0000	0.0000	0.0000	0.0000	0.0000	0.0000	0.0000
1	0.2794	0.0338	0.0029	0.0002	0.0000	0.0000	0.0000	0.0000	0.0000	0.0000
2	0.5405	0.1117	0.0142	0.0013	0.0001	0.0000	0.0000	0.0000	0.0000	0.0000
3	0.7604	0.2503	0.0460	0.0057	0.0005	0.0000	0.0000	0.0000	0.0000	0.0000
4	0.8964	0.4312	0.1121	0.0185	0.0021	0.0002	0.0000	0.0000	0.0000	0.0000
5	0.9622	0.6161	0.2194	0.0480	0.0070	0.0007	0.0001	0.0000	0.0000	0.0000
6	0.9882	0.7702	0.3613	0.1034	0.0194	0.0025	0.0002	0.0000	0.0000	0.0000
7	0.9968	0.8779	0.5188	0.1904	0.0453	0.0073	0.0008	0.0001	0.0000	0.0000
8	0.9992	0.9421	0.6681	0.3073	0.0916	0.0183	0.0025	0.0002	0.0000	0.0000
9	0.9998	0.9755	0.7911	0.4437	0.1637	0.0402	0.0067	0.0008	0.0001	0.0000
10	1.0000	0.9906	0.8801	0.5836	0.2622	0.0789	0.0160	0.0022	0.0002	0.0000
11	1.0000	0.9968	0.9372	0.7107	0.3816	0.1390	0.0342	0.0057	0.0006	0.0000
12	1.0000	0.9990	0.9699	0.8139	0.5110	0.2229	0.0661	0.0133	0.0018	0.0002
13	1.0000	0.9997	0.9868	0.8894	0.6370	0.3279	0.1163	0.0280	0.0045	0.0005
14	1.0000	0.9999	0.9947	0.9393	0.7481	0.4468	0.1878	0.0540	0.0104	0.0013
15	1.0000	1.0000	0.9981	0.9692	0.8369	0.5692	0.2801	0.0955	0.0220	0.0033
16	1.0000	1.0000	0.9993	0.9856	0.9017	0.6839	0.3889	0.1561	0.0427	0.0077
17	1.0000	1.0000	0.9998	0.9937	0.9449	0.7822	0.5060	0.2369	0.0765	0.0164
18	1.0000	1.0000	0.9999	0.9975	0.9713	0.8594	0.6216	0.3356	0.1273	0.0325
19	1.0000	1.0000	1.0000	0.9991	0.9861	0.9152	0.7264	0.4465	0.1974	0.0595
20	1.0000	1.0000	1.0000	0.9997	0.9937	0.9522	0.8139	0.5610	0.2862	0.1013
21	1.0000	1.0000	1.0000	0.9999	0.9974	0.9749	0.8813	0.6701	0.3900	0.1611
22	1.0000	1.0000	1.0000	1.0000	0.9990	0.9877	0.9290	0.7660	0.5019	0.2399
23	1.0000	1.0000	1.0000	1.0000	0.9996	0.9944	0.9604	0.8438	0.6134	0.3359
24	1.0000	1.0000	1.0000	1.0000	0.9999	0.9976	0.9793	0.9022	0.7160	0.4439
25	1.0000	1.0000	1.0000	1.0000	1.0000	0.9991	0.9900	0.9427	0.8034	0.5561
26	1.0000	1.0000	1.0000	1.0000	1.0000	0.9997	0.9955	0.9686	0.8721	0.6641
27	1.0000	1.0000	1.0000	1.0000	1.0000	0.9999	0.9981	0.9840	0.9220	0.7601
28	1.0000	1.0000	1.0000	1.0000	1.0000	1.0000	0.9993	0.9924	0.9556	0.8389
29	1.0000	1.0000	1.0000	1.0000	1.0000	1.0000	0.9997	0.9966	0.9765	0.8987
30	1.0000	1.0000	1.0000	1.0000	1.0000	1.0000	0.9999	0.9986	0.9884	0.9405
31	1.0000	1.0000	1.0000	1.0000	1.0000	1.0000	1.0000	0.9995	0.9947	0.9675
32	1.0000	1.0000	1.0000	1.0000	1.0000	1.0000	1.0000	0.9998	0.9978	0.9836
33	1.0000	1.0000	1.0000	1.0000	1.0000	1.0000	1.0000	0.9999	0.9991	0.9923
34	1.0000	1.0000	1.0000	1.0000	1.0000	1.0000	1.0000	1.0000	0.9997	0.9967
35	1.0000	1.0000	1.0000	1.0000	1.0000	1.0000	1.0000	1.0000	0.9999	0.9987
36	1.0000	1.0000	1.0000	1.0000	1.0000	1.0000	1.0000	1.0000	1.0000	0.9995
37	1.0000	1.0000	1.0000	1.0000	1.0000	1.0000	1.0000	1.0000	1.0000	0.9998
38	1.0000	1.0000	1.0000	1.0000	1.0000	1.0000	1.0000	1.0000	1.0000	1.0000

POISSON CUMULATIVE DISTRIBUTION FUNCTION

The tabulated value is $P(X \leq x)$, where X has a Poisson distribution with parameter λ.

$\lambda =$	0.5	1.0	1.5	2.0	2.5	3.0	3.5	4.0	4.5	5.0
$x = 0$	0.6065	0.3679	0.2231	0.1353	0.0821	0.0498	0.0302	0.0183	0.0111	0.0067
1	0.9098	0.7358	0.5578	0.4060	0.2873	0.1991	0.1359	0.0916	0.0611	0.0404
2	0.9856	0.9197	0.8088	0.6767	0.5438	0.4232	0.3208	0.2381	0.1736	0.1247
3	0.9982	0.9810	0.9344	0.8571	0.7576	0.6472	0.5366	0.4335	0.3423	0.2650
4	0.9998	0.9963	0.9814	0.9473	0.8912	0.8153	0.7254	0.6288	0.5321	0.4405
5	1.0000	0.9994	0.9955	0.9834	0.9580	0.9161	0.8576	0.7851	0.7029	0.6160
6	1.0000	0.9999	0.9991	0.9955	0.9858	0.9665	0.9347	0.8893	0.8311	0.7622
7	1.0000	1.0000	0.9998	0.9989	0.9958	0.9881	0.9733	0.9489	0.9134	0.8666
8	1.0000	1.0000	1.0000	0.9998	0.9989	0.9962	0.9901	0.9786	0.9597	0.9319
9	1.0000	1.0000	1.0000	1.0000	0.9997	0.9989	0.9967	0.9919	0.9829	0.9682
10	1.0000	1.0000	1.0000	1.0000	0.9999	0.9997	0.9990	0.9972	0.9933	0.9863
11	1.0000	1.0000	1.0000	1.0000	1.0000	0.9999	0.9997	0.9991	0.9976	0.9945
12	1.0000	1.0000	1.0000	1.0000	1.0000	1.0000	0.9999	0.9997	0.9992	0.9980
13	1.0000	1.0000	1.0000	1.0000	1.0000	1.0000	1.0000	0.9999	0.9997	0.9993
14	1.0000	1.0000	1.0000	1.0000	1.0000	1.0000	1.0000	1.0000	0.9999	0.9998
15	1.0000	1.0000	1.0000	1.0000	1.0000	1.0000	1.0000	1.0000	1.0000	0.9999
16	1.0000	1.0000	1.0000	1.0000	1.0000	1.0000	1.0000	1.0000	1.0000	1.0000
17	1.0000	1.0000	1.0000	1.0000	1.0000	1.0000	1.0000	1.0000	1.0000	1.0000
18	1.0000	1.0000	1.0000	1.0000	1.0000	1.0000	1.0000	1.0000	1.0000	1.0000
19	1.0000	1.0000	1.0000	1.0000	1.0000	1.0000	1.0000	1.0000	1.0000	1.0000

$\lambda =$	5.5	6.0	6.5	7.0	7.5	8.0	8.5	9.0	9.5	10.0
$x = 0$	0.0041	0.0025	0.0015	0.0009	0.0006	0.0003	0.0002	0.0001	0.0001	0.0000
1	0.0266	0.0174	0.0113	0.0073	0.0047	0.0030	0.0019	0.0012	0.0008	0.0005
2	0.0884	0.0620	0.0430	0.0296	0.0203	0.0138	0.0093	0.0062	0.0042	0.0028
3	0.2017	0.1512	0.1118	0.0818	0.0591	0.0424	0.0301	0.0212	0.0149	0.0103
4	0.3575	0.2851	0.2237	0.1730	0.1321	0.0996	0.0744	0.0550	0.0403	0.0293
5	0.5289	0.4457	0.3690	0.3007	0.2414	0.1912	0.1496	0.1157	0.0885	0.0671
6	0.6860	0.6063	0.5265	0.4497	0.3782	0.3134	0.2562	0.2068	0.1649	0.1301
7	0.8095	0.7440	0.6728	0.5987	0.5246	0.4530	0.3856	0.3239	0.2687	0.2202
8	0.8944	0.8472	0.7916	0.7291	0.6620	0.5925	0.5231	0.4557	0.3918	0.3328
9	0.9462	0.9161	0.8774	0.8305	0.7764	0.7166	0.6530	0.5874	0.5218	0.4579
10	0.9747	0.9574	0.9332	0.9015	0.8622	0.8159	0.7634	0.7060	0.6453	0.5830
11	0.9890	0.9799	0.9661	0.9467	0.9208	0.8881	0.8487	0.8030	0.7520	0.6968
12	0.9955	0.9912	0.9840	0.9730	0.9573	0.9362	0.9091	0.8758	0.8364	0.7916
13	0.9983	0.9964	0.9929	0.9872	0.9784	0.9658	0.9486	0.9261	0.8981	0.8645
14	0.9994	0.9986	0.9970	0.9943	0.9897	0.9827	0.9726	0.9585	0.9400	0.9165
15	0.9998	0.9995	0.9988	0.9976	0.9954	0.9918	0.9862	0.9780	0.9665	0.9513
16	0.9999	0.9998	0.9996	0.9990	0.9980	0.9963	0.9934	0.9889	0.9823	0.9730
17	1.0000	0.9999	0.9998	0.9996	0.9992	0.9984	0.9970	0.9947	0.9911	0.9857
18	1.0000	1.0000	0.9999	0.9999	0.9997	0.9993	0.9987	0.9976	0.9957	0.9928
19	1.0000	1.0000	1.0000	1.0000	0.9999	0.9997	0.9995	0.9989	0.9980	0.9965
20	1.0000	1.0000	1.0000	1.0000	1.0000	0.9999	0.9998	0.9996	0.9991	0.9984
21	1.0000	1.0000	1.0000	1.0000	1.0000	1.0000	0.9999	0.9998	0.9996	0.9993
22	1.0000	1.0000	1.0000	1.0000	1.0000	1.0000	1.0000	0.9999	0.9999	0.9997

Expectation algebra

For independent random variables X and Y

$$E(XY) = E(X)\,E(Y)\,,\ \operatorname{Var}(aX \pm bY) = a^2\operatorname{Var}(X) + b^2\operatorname{Var}(Y)$$

Sampling distributions

For a random sample $X_1, X_2, \dots, X_n$ of n independent observations from a distribution having mean μ and variance σ^2

$\overline{X}$ is an unbiased estimator of μ, with $\operatorname{Var}(\overline{X}) = \dfrac{\sigma^2}{n}$

S^2 is an unbiased estimator of σ^2, where $S^2 = \dfrac{\sum(X_i - \overline{X})^2}{n-1}$

For a random sample of n observations from $N(\mu, \sigma^2)$

$$\frac{\overline{X} - \mu}{\frac{\sigma}{\sqrt{n}}} \sim N(0, 1)$$

For a random sample of n_x observations from $N(\mu_x, \sigma_x^2)$ and, independently, a random sample of n_y observations from $N(\mu_y, \sigma_y^2)$

$$\frac{(\overline{X} - \overline{Y}) - (\mu_x - \mu_y)}{\sqrt{\frac{\sigma_x^2}{n_x} + \frac{\sigma_y^2}{n_y}}} \sim N(0, 1)$$

Correlation and regression

Spearman's rank correlation coefficient is $r_s = 1 - \dfrac{6\sum d^2}{n(n^2 - 1)}$

Non-parametric tests

Goodness-of-fit test and contingency tables: $\sum \dfrac{(O_i - E_i)^2}{E_i} \sim \chi_\nu^2$

PERCENTAGE POINTS OF THE χ^2 DISTRIBUTION

The values in the table are those which a random variable with the χ^2 distribution on ν degrees of freedom exceeds with the probability shown.

ν	0.995	0.990	0.975	0.950	0.900	0.100	0.050	0.025	0.010	0.005
1	0.000	0.000	0.001	0.004	0.016	2.705	3.841	5.024	6.635	7.879
2	0.010	0.020	0.051	0.103	0.211	4.605	5.991	7.378	9.210	10.597
3	0.072	0.115	0.216	0.352	0.584	6.251	7.815	9.348	11.345	12.838
4	0.207	0.297	0.484	0.711	1.064	7.779	9.488	11.143	13.277	14.860
5	0.412	0.554	0.831	1.145	1.610	9.236	11.070	12.832	15.086	16.750
6	0.676	0.872	1.237	1.635	2.204	10.645	12.592	14.449	16.812	18.548
7	0.989	1.239	1.690	2.167	2.833	12.017	14.067	16.013	18.475	20.278
8	1.344	1.646	2.180	2.733	3.490	13.362	15.507	17.535	20.090	21.955
9	1.735	2.088	2.700	3.325	4.168	14.684	16.919	19.023	21.666	23.589
10	2.156	2.558	3.247	3.940	4.865	15.987	18.307	20.483	23.209	25.188
11	2.603	3.053	3.816	4.575	5.580	17.275	19.675	21.920	24.725	26.757
12	3.074	3.571	4.404	5.226	6.304	18.549	21.026	23.337	26.217	28.300
13	3.565	4.107	5.009	5.892	7.042	19.812	22.362	24.736	27.688	29.819
14	4.075	4.660	5.629	6.571	7.790	21.064	23.685	26.119	29.141	31.319
15	4.601	5.229	6.262	7.261	8.547	22.307	24.996	27.488	30.578	32.801
16	5.142	5.812	6.908	7.962	9.312	23.542	26.296	28.845	32.000	34.267
17	5.697	6.408	7.564	8.672	10.085	24.769	27.587	30.191	33.409	35.718
18	6.265	7.015	8.231	9.390	10.865	25.989	28.869	31.526	34.805	37.156
19	6.844	7.633	8.907	10.117	11.651	27.204	30.144	32.852	36.191	38.582
20	7.434	8.260	9.591	10.851	12.443	28.412	31.410	34.170	37.566	39.997
21	8.034	8.897	10.283	11.591	13.240	29.615	32.671	35.479	38.932	41.401
22	8.643	9.542	10.982	12.338	14.042	30.813	33.924	36.781	40.289	42.796
23	9.260	10.196	11.689	13.091	14.848	32.007	35.172	38.076	41.638	44.181
24	9.886	10.856	12.401	13.848	15.659	33.196	36.415	39.364	42.980	45.558
25	10.520	11.524	13.120	14.611	16.473	34.382	37.652	40.646	44.314	46.928
26	11.160	12.198	13.844	15.379	17.292	35.563	38.885	41.923	45.642	48.290
27	11.808	12.879	14.573	16.151	18.114	36.741	40.113	43.194	46.963	49.645
28	12.461	13.565	15.308	16.928	18.939	37.916	41.337	44.461	48.278	50.993
29	13.121	14.256	16.047	17.708	19.768	39.088	42.557	45.722	49.588	52.336
30	13.787	14.953	16.791	18.493	20.599	40.256	43.773	46.979	50.892	53.672

CRITICAL VALUES FOR CORRELATION COEFFICIENTS

These tables concern tests of the hypothesis that a population correlation coefficient ρ is 0. The values in the tables are the minimum values which need to be reached by a sample correlation coefficient in order to be significant at the level shown, on a one-tailed test.

Product-Moment Coefficient						Spearman's Coefficient		
Level					Sample	Level		
0.10	0.05	0.025	0.01	0.005	Level	0.05	0.025	0.01
0.8000	0.9000	0.9500	0.9800	0.9900	4	1.0000	–	–
0.6870	0.8054	0.8783	0.9343	0.9587	5	0.9000	1.0000	1.0000
0.6084	0.7293	0.8114	0.8822	0.9172	6	0.8286	0.8857	0.9429
0.5509	0.6694	0.7545	0.8329	0.8745	7	0.7143	0.7857	0.8929
0.5067	0.6215	0.7067	0.7887	0.8343	8	0.6429	0.7381	0.8333
0.4716	0.5822	0.6664	0.7498	0.7977	9	0.6000	0.7000	0.7833
0.4428	0.5494	0.6319	0.7155	0.7646	10	0.5636	0.6485	0.7455
0.4187	0.5214	0.6021	0.6851	0.7348	11	0.5364	0.6182	0.7091
0.3981	0.4973	0.5760	0.6581	0.7079	12	0.5035	0.5874	0.6783
0.3802	0.4762	0.5529	0.6339	0.6835	13	0.4835	0.5604	0.6484
0.3646	0.4575	0.5324	0.6120	0.6614	14	0.4637	0.5385	0.6264
0.3507	0.4409	0.5140	0.5923	0.6411	15	0.4464	0.5214	0.6036
0.3383	0.4259	0.4973	0.5742	0.6226	16	0.4294	0.5029	0.5824
0.3271	0.4124	0.4821	0.5577	0.6055	17	0.4142	0.4877	0.5662
0.3170	0.4000	0.4683	0.5425	0.5897	18	0.4014	0.4716	0.5501
0.3077	0.3887	0.4555	0.5285	0.5751	19	0.3912	0.4596	0.5351
0.2992	0.3783	0.4438	0.5155	0.5614	20	0.3805	0.4466	0.5218
0.2914	0.3687	0.4329	0.5034	0.5487	21	0.3701	0.4364	0.5091
0.2841	0.3598	0.4227	0.4921	0.5368	22	0.3608	0.4252	0.4975
0.2774	0.3515	0.4133	0.4815	0.5256	23	0.3528	0.4160	0.4862
0.2711	0.3438	0.4044	0.4716	0.5151	24	0.3443	0.4070	0.4757
0.2653	0.3365	0.3961	0.4622	0.5052	25	0.3369	0.3977	0.4662
0.2598	0.3297	0.3882	0.4534	0.4958	26	0.3306	0.3901	0.4571
0.2546	0.3233	0.3809	0.4451	0.4869	27	0.3242	0.3828	0.4487
0.2497	0.3172	0.3739	0.4372	0.4785	28	0.3180	0.3755	0.4401
0.2451	0.3115	0.3673	0.4297	0.4705	29	0.3118	0.3685	0.4325
0.2407	0.3061	0.3610	0.4226	0.4629	30	0.3063	0.3624	0.4251
0.2070	0.2638	0.3120	0.3665	0.4026	40	0.2640	0.3128	0.3681
0.1843	0.2353	0.2787	0.3281	0.3610	50	0.2353	0.2791	0.3293
0.1678	0.2144	0.2542	0.2997	0.3301	60	0.2144	0.2545	0.3005
0.1550	0.1982	0.2352	0.2776	0.3060	70	0.1982	0.2354	0.2782
0.1448	0.1852	0.2199	0.2597	0.2864	80	0.1852	0.2201	0.2602
0.1364	0.1745	0.2072	0.2449	0.2702	90	0.1745	0.2074	0.2453
0.1292	0.1654	0.1966	0.2324	0.2565	100	0.1654	0.1967	0.2327

RANDOM NUMBERS

86	13	84	10	07	30	39	05	97	96	88	07	37	26	04	89	13	48	19	20
60	78	48	12	99	47	09	46	91	33	17	21	03	94	79	00	08	50	40	16
78	48	06	37	82	26	01	06	64	65	94	41	17	26	74	66	61	93	24	97
80	56	90	79	66	94	18	40	97	79	93	20	41	51	25	04	20	71	76	04
99	09	39	25	66	31	70	56	30	15	52	17	87	55	31	11	10	68	98	23
56	32	32	72	91	65	97	36	56	61	12	79	95	17	57	16	53	58	96	36
66	02	49	93	97	44	99	15	56	86	80	57	11	78	40	23	58	40	86	14
31	77	53	94	05	93	56	14	71	23	60	46	05	33	23	72	93	10	81	23
98	79	72	43	14	76	54	77	66	29	84	09	88	56	75	86	41	67	04	42
50	97	92	15	10	01	57	01	87	33	73	17	70	18	40	21	24	20	66	62
90	51	94	50	12	48	88	95	09	34	09	30	22	27	25	56	40	76	01	59
31	99	52	24	13	43	27	88	11	39	41	65	00	84	13	06	31	79	74	97
22	96	23	34	46	12	67	11	48	06	99	24	14	83	78	37	65	73	39	47
06	84	55	41	27	06	74	59	14	29	20	14	45	75	31	16	05	41	22	96
08	64	89	30	25	25	71	35	33	31	04	56	12	67	03	74	07	16	49	32
86	87	62	43	15	11	76	49	79	13	78	80	93	89	09	57	07	14	40	74
94	44	97	13	77	04	35	02	12	76	60	91	93	40	81	06	85	85	72	84
63	25	55	14	66	47	99	90	02	90	83	43	16	01	19	69	11	78	87	16
11	22	83	98	15	21	18	57	53	42	91	91	26	52	89	13	86	00	47	61
01	70	10	83	94	71	13	67	11	12	36	54	53	32	90	43	79	01	95	15

Sampling distributions

For a random sample of n observations from $N(\mu, \sigma^2)$.

$$\frac{(n-1)S^2}{\sigma^2} \sim \chi^2_{n-1}$$

$$\frac{\overline{X} - \mu}{\frac{S}{\sqrt{n}}} \sim t_{n-1}$$

For a random sample of n_x observations from $N(\mu_x, \sigma_x^2)$ and, independently, a random sample of n_y observations from $N(\mu_y, \sigma_y^2)$

$$\frac{\frac{S_x^2}{\sigma_x^2}}{\frac{S_y^2}{\sigma_y^2}} \sim F_{n_x - 1,\, n_y - 1}$$

If $\sigma_x^2 = \sigma_y^2 = \sigma^2$(unknown) then

$$\frac{(\overline{X} - \overline{Y}) - (\mu_x - \mu_y)}{\sqrt{S_p^2\left(\frac{1}{n_x} + \frac{1}{n_y}\right)}} \sim t_{n_x + n_y - 2} \qquad \text{where} \qquad S_p^2 = \frac{(n_x - 1)S_x^2 + (n_y - 1)S_y^2}{n_x + n_y - 2}$$

PERCENTAGE POINTS OF STUDENT'S t DISTRIBUTION

The values in the table are those which a random variable with Student's t distribution on ν degrees of freedom exceeds with the probability shown.

ν	0.10	0.05	0.025	0.01	0.005
1	3.078	6.314	12.706	31.821	63.657
2	1.886	2.920	4.303	6.965	9.925
3	1.638	2.353	3.182	4.541	5.841
4	1.533	2.132	2.776	3.747	4.604
5	1.476	2.015	2.571	3.365	4.032
6	1.440	1.943	2.447	3.143	3.707
7	1.415	1.895	2.365	2.998	3.499
8	1.397	1.860	2.306	2.896	3.355
9	1.383	1.833	2.262	2.821	3.250
10	1.372	1.812	2.228	2.764	3.169
11	1.363	1.796	2.201	2.718	3.106
12	1.356	1.782	2.179	2.681	3.055
13	1.350	1.771	2.160	2.650	3.012
14	1.345	1.761	2.145	2.624	2.977
15	1.341	1.753	2.131	2.602	2.947
16	1.337	1.746	2.120	2.583	2.921
17	1.333	1.740	2.110	2.567	2.898
18	1.330	1.734	2.101	2.552	2.878
19	1.328	1.729	2.093	2.539	2.861
20	1.325	1.725	2.086	2.528	2.845
21	1.323	1.721	2.080	2.518	2.831
22	1.321	1.717	2.074	2.508	2.819
23	1.319	1.714	2.069	2.500	2.807
24	1.318	1.711	2.064	2.492	2.797
25	1.316	1.708	2.060	2.485	2.787
26	1.315	1.706	2.056	2.479	2.779
27	1.314	1.703	2.052	2.473	2.771
28	1.313	1.701	2.048	2.467	2.763
29	1.311	1.699	2.045	2.462	2.756
30	1.310	1.697	2.042	2.457	2.750
32	1.309	1.694	2.037	2.449	2.738
34	1.307	1.691	2.032	2.441	2.728
36	1.306	1.688	2.028	2.435	2.719
38	1.304	1.686	2.024	2.429	2.712
40	1.303	1.684	2.021	2.423	2.704
45	1.301	1.679	2.014	2.412	2.690
50	1.299	1.676	2.009	2.403	2.678
55	1.297	1.673	2.004	2.396	2.668
60	1.296	1.671	2.000	2.390	2.660
70	1.294	1.667	1.994	2.381	2.648
80	1.292	1.664	1.990	2.374	2.639
90	1.291	1.662	1.987	2.369	2.632
100	1.290	1.660	1.984	2.364	2.626
110	1.289	1.659	1.982	2.361	2.621
120	1.289	1.658	1.980	2.358	2.617

PERCENTAGE POINTS OF THE *F* DISTRIBUTION

The values in the table are those which a random variable with the *F* distribution on ν_1 and ν_2 degrees of freedom exceeds with probability 0.05 or 0.01.

Probability	ν_2/ν_1	1	2	3	4	5	6	8	10	12	24	∞
0.05	1	161.4	199.5	215.7	224.6	230.2	234.0	238.9	241.9	243.9	249.1	254.3
	2	18.51	19.00	19.16	19.25	19.30	19.33	19.37	19.40	19.41	19.46	19.50
	3	10.13	9.55	9.28	9.12	9.01	8.94	8.85	8.79	8.74	8.64	8.53
	4	7.71	6.94	6.59	6.39	6.26	6.16	6.04	5.96	5.91	5.77	5.63
	5	6.61	5.79	5.41	5.19	5.05	4.95	4.82	4.74	4.68	4.53	4.37
	6	5.99	5.14	4.76	4.53	4.39	4.28	4.15	4.06	4.00	3.84	3.67
	7	5.59	4.74	4.35	4.12	3.97	3.87	3.73	3.64	3.57	3.41	3.23
	8	5.32	4.46	4.07	3.84	3.69	3.58	3.44	3.35	3.28	3.12	2.93
	9	5.12	4.26	3.86	3.63	3.48	3.37	3.23	3.14	3.07	2.90	2.71
	10	4.96	4.10	3.71	3.48	3.33	3.22	3.07	2.98	2.91	2.74	2.54
	11	4.84	3.98	3.59	3.36	3.20	3.09	2.95	2.85	2.79	2.61	2.40
	12	4.75	3.89	3.49	3.26	3.11	3.00	2.85	2.75	2.69	2.51	2.30
	14	4.60	3.74	3.34	3.11	2.96	2.85	2.70	2.60	2.53	2.35	2.13
	16	4.49	3.63	3.24	3.01	2.85	2.74	2.59	2.49	2.42	2.24	2.01
	18	4.41	3.55	3.16	2.93	2.77	2.66	2.51	2.41	2.34	2.15	1.92
	20	4.35	3.49	3.10	2.87	2.71	2.60	2.45	2.35	2.28	2.08	1.84
	25	4.24	3.39	2.99	2.76	2.60	2.49	2.34	2.24	2.16	1.96	1.71
	30	4.17	3.32	2.92	2.69	2.53	2.42	2.27	2.16	2.09	1.89	1.62
	40	4.08	3.23	2.84	2.61	2.45	2.34	2.18	2.08	2.00	1.79	1.51
	60	4.00	3.15	2.76	2.53	2.37	2.25	2.10	1.99	1.92	1.70	1.39
	120	3.92	3.07	2.68	2.45	2.29	2.18	2.02	1.91	1.83	1.61	1.25
	∞	3.84	3.00	2.60	2.37	2.21	2.10	1.94	1.83	1.75	1.52	1.00
0.01	1	4052.	5000.	5403.	5625.	5764.	5859.	5982.	6056.	6106.	6235.	6366.
	2	98.50	99.00	99.17	99.25	99.30	99.33	99.37	99.40	99.42	99.46	99.50
	3	34.12	30.82	29.46	28.71	28.24	27.91	27.49	27.23	27.05	26.60	26.13
	4	21.20	18.00	16.69	15.98	15.52	15.21	14.80	14.55	14.37	13.93	13.45
	5	16.26	13.27	12.06	11.39	10.97	10.67	10.29	10.05	9.89	9.47	9.02
	6	13.70	10.90	9.78	9.15	8.75	8.47	8.10	7.87	7.72	7.31	6.88
	7	12.20	9.55	8.45	7.85	7.46	7.19	6.84	6.62	6.47	6.07	5.65
	8	11.30	8.65	7.59	7.01	6.63	6.37	6.03	5.81	5.67	5.28	4.86
	9	10.60	8.02	6.99	6.42	6.06	5.80	5.47	5.26	5.11	4.73	4.31
	10	10.00	7.56	6.55	5.99	5.64	5.39	5.06	4.85	4.17	4.33	3.91
	11	9.65	7.21	6.22	5.67	5.32	5.07	4.74	4.54	4.40	4.02	3.60
	12	9.33	6.93	5.95	5.41	5.06	4.82	4.50	4.30	4.16	3.78	3.36
	14	8.86	6.51	5.56	5.04	4.70	4.46	4.14	3.94	3.80	3.43	3.00
	16	8.53	6.23	5.29	4.77	4.44	4.20	3.89	3.69	3.55	3.18	2.75
	18	8.29	6.01	5.09	4.58	4.25	4.01	3.71	3.51	3.37	3.00	2.57
	20	8.10	5.85	4.94	4.43	4.10	3.87	3.56	3.37	3.23	2.86	2.42
	25	7.77	5.57	4.68	4.18	3.86	3.63	3.32	3.13	2.99	2.62	2.17
	30	7.56	5.39	4.51	4.02	3.70	3.47	3.17	2.98	2.84	2.47	2.01
	40	7.31	5.18	4.31	3.83	3.51	3.29	2.99	2.80	2.66	2.29	1.80
	60	7.08	4.98	4.13	3.65	3.34	3.12	2.82	2.63	2.50	2.12	1.60
	120	6.85	4.79	3.95	3.48	3.17	2.96	2.66	2.47	2.34	1.95	1.38
	∞	6.63	4.61	3.78	3.32	3.02	2.80	2.51	2.32	2.18	1.79	1.00

If an *upper* percentage point of the *F* distribution on ν_1 and ν_2 degrees of freedom is f, then the corresponding *lower* percentage point of the *F* distribution on ν_1 and ν_2 degrees of freedom is $\frac{1}{f}$.

Answers

Exercise 1A

1 a $X \geqslant 6$
  b 0.0197, 0.9527
2 a $X \leqslant 1$
  b 0.0076, 0.9757
3 a $\{X \leqslant 1\} \cup \{X \geqslant 9\}$
  b 0.0278, 0.9519
4 a $X \geqslant 11$
  b 0.0426, 0.9015
5 a $X = 0$
  b 0.0111, 0.9698
6 a $\{X \leqslant 3\} \cup \{X \geqslant 16\}$
  b 0.9494

Exercise 1B

1 a $\bar{x} > 51.5605...$
  b 0.01
  c 0.0162, awrt 0.016
2 a $\bar{x} < 29.178$
  b 0.05
  c 0.0869, awrt 0.087 ~ 0.088
3 a $\{\bar{X} < 37.939\} \cup \{\bar{X} > 42.061\}$
  b 0.01
  c 0.5319, awrt 0.53
4 a $\bar{x} < 14.608$ or $\bar{x} > 15.392$
  b 0.1492, awrt 0.1492
5 a $\bar{x} > 42.4025...$
  b 0.6103, awrt 0.61
  c Only way of reducing P(Type II) error and changing significance level is to increase sample size.

Exercise 1C

1 a $\bar{x} > 20.9869...$
  b 0.3783, awrt 0.378
2 a 0.0196
  b 0.0247
3 a 0.0111
  b 0.0166 (3 s.f.)
4 0.3522, awrt 0.352 ~ 0.353
5 a 0.0548
  b 0.8791
  c The test is more powerful for values of p further away from $p = 0.3$
6 a Type I error is when H_0 is rejected when H_0 is in fact true.
  b 0.0571

Exercise 1D

1 a 0.0430
  c $\lambda = 2 \Rightarrow s = 0.6767 = 0.68$ (2 d.p.)
    $\lambda = 5 \Rightarrow t = 0.1247 = 0.12$ (2 d.p.)
  d

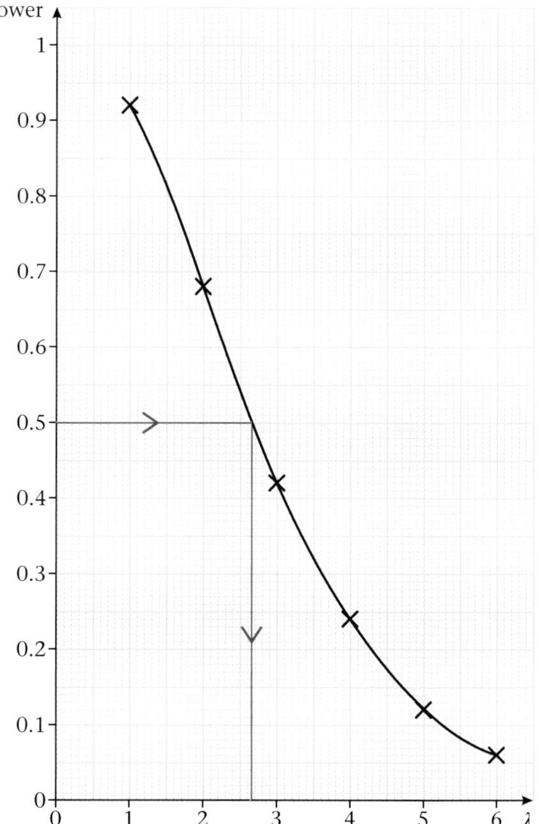

  e Correct conclusion is arrived at when $\lambda = 6.5$, H_0 is accepted. So since size is 0.0430 probability of accepting $\lambda = 6.5$ is $0.957 \therefore \lambda = 6.5$
    or for $\lambda < 6.5$, correct conclusion is to reject H_0.
    So require where power > 0.5 i.e. $\lambda < 2.65$ (from graph).

2 a 0.0421
  c 0.2528

3 a 0.0547
  b 0.6778
  c The test is more powerful for values of p further away from 0.4

4 a 0.0547
  b $(1 - p)^{10} + 10p(1 - p)^9 + 45p^2(1 - p)^8$
  c 0.06152
  d $(1 - p)^5 [2 - (1 - p)^5]$
  e $p = 0.25 \Rightarrow \text{power}_A = 0.5256$
    $p = 0.35 \Rightarrow \text{power}_B = 0.2616$
  f Use test A as this is always more powerful.

Exercise 1E

1 a $\text{Var}(\hat{\mu}_1) = \dfrac{\sigma^2}{3}$ $\qquad \text{Var}(\hat{\mu}_2) = \dfrac{3\sigma^2}{8}$

b Recommend $\hat{\mu}_1 \therefore \text{Var}(\hat{\mu}_1) < \text{Var}(\hat{\mu}_2)$

2 a unbiased

b bias $= -\frac{1}{4}\mu$

c unbiased

d unbiased

e bias $= \frac{1}{5}\mu$

3 a $\frac{13}{32}\sigma^2$

b Estimator is biased so would not prefer

c $\frac{5}{9}\sigma^2$ or $0.5550\sigma^2$

d $\frac{1}{3}\sigma^2$ or $0.333\sigma^2$

e Estimator is biased.
Best estimator is unbiased with smallest variance.
Since $\frac{1}{3}\sigma^2 < \frac{13}{32}\sigma^2 < \frac{5}{9}\sigma^2$
$\therefore \frac{1}{3}(X_1 + X_2 + X_3)$

4 a i $\dfrac{a}{2}$ $\qquad$ **ii** unbiased $\qquad$ **iii** bias $= 3a$

b i $\dfrac{a^2}{4}$ $\qquad$ **ii** $\dfrac{a^2}{9}$ $\qquad$ **iii** $2a^2$

c use $\frac{2}{3}(X_1 + X_2 + X_3)$ since it is unbiased (and has smallest variance)

d $\hat{a} = 5.1\dot{3}$

5 $X = \dfrac{m}{50}$ $\quad \therefore$ for $\hat{m}$ to be unbiased you need $c = 50$

7 a $p(1-p)$ or pq

c $pq(a_1{}^2 + a_2{}^2 + a_3{}^2)$

d i $\dfrac{9pq}{25}$

ii not unbiased

iii Best estimator is $\frac{1}{5}X_1 + \frac{2}{5}X_2 + \frac{2}{5}X_3$ since it is unbiased and has smaller variance $\left(\frac{9}{25} < \frac{41}{81}\right)$

Exercise 1F

1 b $\hat{p} = \frac{9}{25}$

2 b $2\overline{X}$ is a consistent estimator of a.

6 $X \sim B(n, p)$ $\qquad Y \sim B(n, p)$
$E(X) = \mu = np$ $\qquad \text{Var}(X) = \sigma^2 = np(1-p)$

b $\because \frac{25}{49} > \frac{1}{2}$
$\therefore$ Choose $\dfrac{\overline{X} + \overline{Y}}{2n}$ since it has smaller variance.

Mixed exercise 1G

1 a $X \geqslant 9$

b 0.0422

c 0.3036

2 a $X = 0$

b 0.0302

c 0.0498

3 a $\overline{X} < 6.614...$ or $\overline{X} > 9.3859...$

b 0.05

c awrt $0.707 \sim 0.708$

d $0.293 \sim 0.292$

4 a 0.0866

b i $r = 1 - 0.9489 = 0.0511$
$s = 1 - 0.7440 = 0.2560$
$t = 1 - 0.3239 = 0.6761$

ii Power

(Graph: Power against λ, λ from 0 to 10, Power from 0 to 1)

5 a 0.0424

b Power $= P(X \leqslant 3 \mid X \sim B(15, p))$
$p = 0.2 \Rightarrow s = 0.6482$
$p = 0.4 \Rightarrow t = 0.0905$

c

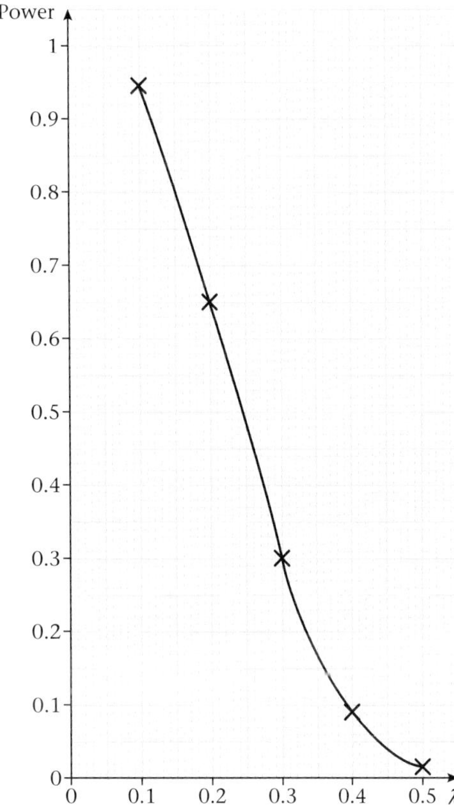

6 a $c = \frac{25}{2}$

b $\dfrac{2m}{25}$

7 If 3 balls are selected $E(X) = \dfrac{3m}{25}$

If 4 balls are selected $E(Y) = \dfrac{4m}{25}$

b $\dfrac{X+Y}{7}$ $\because$ variance is smallest.

8 a $H_0: \lambda = 2$ (Quality the same) $H_1: \lambda > 2$ (Quality is poorer)

b critical region $X \geqslant 5$

c 0.3712

9 a $H_0: \lambda = 2$ $H_1: \lambda > 2$

b critical region $X \geqslant 5$

c 0.1847

d critical region $X \geqslant 11$

e 0.294

f Second test is more powerful as it uses more days.

10 a 0.0620

c $s = 0.6767$
$t = 0.1247$

d

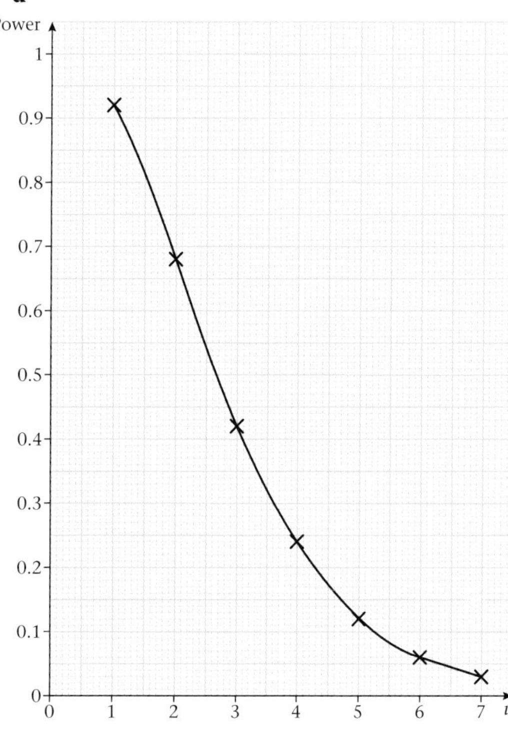

e $\mu < 1.55$

11 a $E(X) = p$
$E(X^2) = p$, $\text{Var}(X) = p(1-p)$

b $a_1 + a_2 + a_3 = 1$

c $(a_1^2 + a_2^2 + a_3^2)pq$

d $\frac{1}{6}X_1 + \frac{1}{3}X_2 + \frac{1}{2}X_3$

12 $X \sim B(n, p) \Rightarrow \mu_X = np$ $\sigma_X^2 = np(1-p)$
$Y \sim B(m, p) \Rightarrow \mu_Y = mp$ $\sigma_Y^2 = mp(1-p)$

b $\text{Var}(\hat{p}_1) = \dfrac{(m+n)(p(1-p)}{4mn}$

$\text{Var}(\hat{p}_2) = \dfrac{p(1-p)}{n+m}$

c $\therefore$ use $\hat{p}_2$ $\because$ unbiased and has smaller variance.

13 a $E(\tau_1) =$ unbiased

$E(\tau_2) =$ bias $= \tau\left(\dfrac{\sqrt{3}}{3} - 1\right)$

$E(\tau_3) =$ unbiased

b $\text{Var}(\tau_1) = \dfrac{\tau^2}{6}$

$\text{Var}(\tau_2) = \dfrac{\tau^2}{6}$

$\text{Var}(\tau_3) = \dfrac{\tau^2}{8}$

c τ_3 is best since it is unbiased and it has smallest variance

d τ_2 is worst since it is biased (and variance is just same as τ_1)

Exercise 2A

1 a $P(X > t) = 0.025$ when $t = 2.179$ so $P(X < t) = 0.025$ when $t = -2.179$

b $P(X > t) = 0.025$ when $t = 1.782$

c $P(X > t) = 0.025$ when $t = 2.179$
$P(|X| > t) = 0.95$ when $|t| = 2.179$

2 a 2.479 **b** 1.706

3 a $P(Y > t) = 0.05$ when $t = 1.812$ so $P(Y < t) = 0.95$ when $t = 1.812$

b $P(Y > t) = 0.005$ when $t = 2.738$ so $P(Y > t) = 0.005$ when $t = -2.738$

c $P(Y > t) = 0.025$ when $t = 2.571$ so $P(Y < t) = 0.025$ when $t = -2.571$

d $P(Y > t) = 0.01$, when $t = 2.583$, and $P(Y < t) = 0.01$ when $t = -2.583$
so $P(|Y| < t) = 0.98$ when $|t| = 2.583$

e $P(Y > t) = 0.05$ when $t = 1.734$ and $P(Y < t) = 0.05$ when $t = -1.734$
so $P(|Y| > t) = 0.10$ when $|t| = 1.734$

Exercise 2B

1 $\bar{x} = 20.95$ $s = 3.4719\ldots$ $n = 8$ $v = 7$

confidence limits $= x \pm t_{(n-1)}\left(\dfrac{\alpha}{2}\right) \times \dfrac{s}{\sqrt{n}}$

$= 20.95 \pm 1.895 \times \dfrac{3.4719\ldots}{\sqrt{8}} = 18.624$ and 23.276

Confidence interval = (18.624, 23.276)

2 $\bar{x} = 12.4$ $s = \sqrt{21}$ $n = 16$ $v = 15$

confidence limits $= \bar{x} \pm t_{(n-1)}\left(\dfrac{\alpha}{2}\right) \times \dfrac{s}{\sqrt{n}}$

$= 12.4 \pm 2.131 \times \dfrac{\sqrt{21}}{\sqrt{16}} = 9.9586$ and 14.8413...

Confidence interval = (9.959, 14.841)

3 a $\bar{x} = 179.333333$ $s = 5.5015\ldots$ $n = 6$ $v = 5$

confidence limits $= \bar{x} \pm t_{(n-1)}\left(\dfrac{\alpha}{2}\right) \times \dfrac{s}{\sqrt{n}}$

$= 179.333 \pm 2.015 \times \dfrac{5.5015\ldots}{\sqrt{6}}$

$= 174.808$ and 183.859

Confidence interval = (174.808, 183.859)

b confidence limits $= \bar{x} \pm t_{(n-1)}\left(\dfrac{\alpha}{2}\right) \times \dfrac{s}{\sqrt{n}}$

$= 179.333 \pm 2.571 \times \dfrac{5.5015\ldots}{\sqrt{6}}$

$= 173.559$ and 185.108

Confidence interval = (173.559, 185.108)

4 $\bar{x} = 10.36$ $s = 0.73363...$ $n = 10$ $v = 9$

$$\text{confidence limits} = \bar{x} \pm t_{(n-1)}\left(\frac{\alpha}{2}\right) \times \frac{s}{\sqrt{n}}$$
$$= 10.36 \pm 2.821 \times \frac{0.73363...}{\sqrt{10}}$$
$$= 9.706 \text{ and } 11.014$$

Confidence interval = (9.706, 11.014)

5 $\bar{x} = \frac{224.1}{8} = 28.0125$ $s^2 = \frac{1}{7}\left\{6337.39 - \frac{224.1^2}{8}\right\}$
$= 8.54125$
$s = 2.92254...$ $n = 8$ $v = 7$

$$\text{confidence limits} = \bar{x} \pm t_{(n-1)}\left(\frac{\alpha}{2}\right) \times \frac{s}{\sqrt{n}}$$
$$= 28.0125 \pm 3.499 \times \frac{2.92254...}{\sqrt{8}}$$
$$= 24.397 \text{ and } 31.628$$

Confidence interval = (24.397, 31.628)

6 $\bar{x} = 122$ $s = \sqrt{225} = 25$ $v = 25$

$$\text{confidence limits} = \bar{x} \pm t_{(n-1)}\left(\frac{\alpha}{2}\right) \times \frac{s}{\sqrt{n}}$$
$$= 122 \pm 2.060 \times \frac{\sqrt{225}}{\sqrt{26}}$$
$$= 115.940 \text{ and } 128.060$$

Confidence interval = (115.94, 128.06)

Exercise 2C

1 $\bar{x} = 11.4$ $s = 1.816....$
$H_0 : \mu = 11$ $H_0 : \mu > 11$
Critical region $t > 2.132$

$$\text{Test statistic } t = \frac{\bar{x} - \mu}{\frac{s}{\sqrt{n}}} = \frac{11.4 - 11.0}{\frac{1.816...}{\sqrt{5}}} = 0.492$$

The result is not in critical region.
No evidence that μ is not 11

2 $\bar{x} = 17.1$ $s = 2$
$H_0 : \mu = 19$ $H_1 : \mu < 19$
Critical region $t < -2.473$

$$\text{Test statistic } t = \frac{\bar{x} - \mu}{\frac{s}{\sqrt{n}}} = \frac{17.1 - 19}{\frac{2}{\sqrt{28}}} = -5.027$$

The result is in the critical region.
There is evidence that μ is < 19

3 $\bar{x} = 3.26$ $s = 0.8$
$H_0 : \mu = 3$ $H_1 : \mu \neq 3$
Critical values $\pm$ 2.179
Critical region $t < -2.179$ or $t > 2.179$

$$\text{Test statistic } t = \frac{\bar{x} - \mu}{\frac{s}{\sqrt{n}}} = \frac{3.25 - 3}{\frac{0.8}{\sqrt{13}}} = 1.172$$

The result is not in the critical region.
There is no evidence that μ is not 3

4 $\bar{x} = 98.2$ $s = 15.744...$
$H_0 : \mu = 100$ $H_1 : \mu \neq 100$
Critical region < -2.145 or > 2.145

$$\text{Test statistic } t = \frac{\bar{x} - \mu}{\frac{s}{\sqrt{n}}} = \frac{98.2 - 100}{\frac{15.74...}{\sqrt{15}}} = -0.443$$

The result is not in the critical region.
There is no evidence that μ is not 100

5 $x = 1048.75$ $s = 95.2346...$
$H_0 : \mu = 1000$ $H_1 : \mu > 1000$
Critical region $t > 1.895$

$$\text{Test statistic } t = \frac{\bar{x} - \mu}{\frac{s}{\sqrt{n}}} = \frac{1048.75 - 1000}{\frac{95.234...}{\sqrt{8}}} = 1.448$$

The result is not in the critical region.
There is no evidence that μ is not 1000

6 $\bar{x} = 6.4857...$ $s^2 = 0.853626...$ $s = 0.923919...$
$H_0 : \mu = 6$ $H_1 : \mu > 6$
Critical region $t > 2.160$

$$\text{Test statistic } t = \frac{\bar{x} - \mu}{\frac{s}{\sqrt{n}}} = \frac{6.4857142 - 6}{\frac{0.923919...}{\sqrt{14}}} = 1.967$$

The result is not in the critical region.
There is no evidence supporting manufacturer's claim.

7 $\bar{x} = 1.085$ $s^2 = \frac{28.4 - 20 \times 1.085^2}{19} = 0.2555...$
$s = 0.5055...$
$H_0 : \mu = 1.00$ $H_1 : \mu < 1.00$
Critical values $t < -1.328$

$$\text{Test statistic } t = \frac{\bar{x} - \mu}{\frac{s}{\sqrt{n}}} = \frac{1.085 - 1}{\frac{0.5055...}{\sqrt{20}}} = 0.752$$

The result is not in the critical region.
There is no evidence that μ is not 1.00

Exercise 2D

1 Confidence interval $= \left(\frac{(n-1)s^2}{\chi^2_{n-1}\left(\frac{\alpha}{2}\right)}, \frac{(n-1)s^2}{\chi^2_{n-1}\left(1 - \frac{\alpha}{2}\right)}\right)$

$$= \left(\frac{14 \times 4.8}{26.119}, \frac{14 \times 4.8}{5.628}\right)$$
$$= (2.573, 11.938)$$

2 $\bar{x} = 6.62$ $s^2 = \frac{1}{19}\left(884.3 - \frac{132^2}{20}\right) = 0.4111...$

Confidence interval $= \left(\frac{(n-1)s^2}{\chi^2_{n-1}\left(\frac{\alpha}{2}\right)}, \frac{(n-1)s^2}{\chi^2_{n-1}\left(1 - \frac{\alpha}{2}\right)}\right)$

$$= \left(\frac{19 \times 0.411...}{30.114}, \frac{19 \times 0.411...}{10.117}\right)$$
$$= (0.259, 0.772)$$

3 $\bar{x} = 2.878...$ $s^2 = 0.458...$

Confidence interval $= \left(\frac{(n-1)s^2}{\chi^2_{n-1}\left(\frac{\alpha}{2}\right)}, \frac{(n-1)s^2}{\chi^2_{n-1}\left(1 - \frac{\alpha}{2}\right)}\right)$

$$= \left(\frac{13 \times 0.458...}{24.736}, \frac{13 \times 0.458...}{5.009}\right)$$
$$= (0.241, 1.191)$$

4 $\bar{x} = 8.12$ $s^2 = 2.037...$ $s = 1.427...$

a Confidence interval $= x \pm t_{n-1}\left(\frac{\alpha}{2}\right) \times \frac{s}{\sqrt{n}} =$

$$\left(8.12 - 2.776 \times \frac{1.427...}{\sqrt{5}}, 8.12 + 2.776 \times \frac{1.427...}{\sqrt{5}}\right)$$
$$= (6.348, 9.892)$$

b Confidence interval $= \left(\frac{(n-1)s^2}{\chi^2_{n-1}\left(\frac{\alpha}{2}\right)}, \frac{(n-1)s^2}{\chi^2_{n-1}\left(1 - \frac{\alpha}{2}\right)}\right)$

$$= \left(\frac{4 \times 2.037}{11.143}, \frac{4 \times 2.037}{0.484}\right)$$
$$= (0.731, 16.835)$$

5 a $\bar{x} = 62.1 \quad s^2 = \frac{1}{9}\left(38\,938 - \frac{621^2}{10}\right) = 41.544...$

$s = 6.445...$

i Confidence interval $= x \pm t_{n-1}\left(\frac{\alpha}{2}\right) \times \frac{s}{\sqrt{n}} =$

$\left(62.1 - 1.833 \times \frac{6.445...}{\sqrt{10}}, 62.1 + 1.833 \times \frac{6.445...}{\sqrt{10}}\right)$

$= (58.364, 65.836)$

ii Confidence interval $= \left(\frac{(n-1)s^2}{\chi^2_{n-1}\left(\frac{\alpha}{2}\right)}, \frac{(n-1)s^2}{\chi^2_{n-1}\left(1-\frac{\alpha}{2}\right)}\right)$

$= \left(\frac{4 \times 41.544...}{16.919}, \frac{9 \times 41.544...}{3.325}\right)$

$= (22.099, 112.420)$

b Normal distribution

6 $\bar{x} = 238 \quad s = 17.694... \quad s^2 = 313.111...$

Confidence interval mean

$= \left(\bar{x} - t_{n-1}\left(\frac{\alpha}{2}\right) \times \frac{s}{\sqrt{n}}, \bar{x} + t_{n-1}\left(\frac{\alpha}{2}\right) \times \frac{s}{\sqrt{n}}\right)$

$= \left(238 - 2.262 \times \frac{17.694...}{\sqrt{10}}, 238 - 2.262 \times \frac{17.694...}{\sqrt{10}}\right)$

$= (225.343, 250.657)$

Confidence interval variance

$= \left(\frac{(n-1)s^2}{\chi^2_{n-1}\left(\frac{\alpha}{2}\right)}, \frac{(n-1)s^2}{\chi^2_{n-1}\left(1-\frac{\alpha}{2}\right)}\right)$

$= \left(\frac{9 \times 313.111...}{19.023}, \frac{9 \times 313.11...}{2.700}\right)$

$= (148.136, 1043.704)$

Exercise 2E

1 a $\bar{x} = 16.605 \quad s^2 = \frac{5583.63 - 20(16.605)^2}{19} = 3.637...$

b $H_0: \sigma^2 = 1.5 \quad H_1: \sigma^2 > 1.5$

Critical region $\geqslant 30.144$

Test statistic $= \frac{(n-1)s^2}{\sigma^2} = \frac{19 \times 3.637...}{1.5} = 46.072$

The test statistic is in the critical region.

There is evidence to suggest $\sigma^2 > 1.5$

2 $\bar{x} = 0.337 \quad s^2 = 0.00286...$

$H_0: \sigma^2 = 1.5 \quad H_1: \sigma^2 < 0.09$

Critical region $\leqslant 2.700$

Test statistic $= \frac{(n-1)s^2}{\sigma^2} = \frac{9 \times 0.00286...}{0.09} = 0.287$

The test statistic is in the critical region.

There is evidence to suggest that variance is less than 0.09

3 $H_0: \sigma^2 = 4.1 \quad H_1: \sigma^2 \neq 4.1$

$\bar{x} = 5.74 \quad s^2 = 6.940...$

Critical region <2.7 and >19.023

Test statistic $= \frac{(n-1)s^2}{\sigma^2} = \frac{9 \times 6.940...}{4.1} = 15.235$

The test statistic is not in the critical region.

There is no evidence the variance does not = 4.1

4 $H_0: \sigma^2 = 1.12^2 \quad H_1: \sigma^2 \neq 1.12^2$

Critical region < 8.907 and >32.852

Test statistic $= \frac{(n-1)s^2}{\sigma^2} = \frac{19 \times 1.15...}{1.12^2} = 17.419$

The test statistic is not in the critical region.

There is no evidence the variance does not = 1.12

5 a $\bar{x} = \frac{149.941}{15} = 9.996...,$

$s^2 = \frac{1498.83 - 15 \times 9.996...^2}{14} = 0.0006977...$

$s = 0.0264$

b i $H_0: \mu = 10 \quad H_1: \mu \neq 10$

Critical region < -2.145 and > 2.145.

Test statistic $= \frac{\bar{x} - \mu}{\frac{s}{\sqrt{n}}} = \frac{9.996... - 10}{\frac{0.0264...}{\sqrt{15}}} = -0.587$

The test statistic is not in the critical region.

There is no evidence that the mean does not = 10

ii $H_0: \sigma^2 = 0.04 \quad H_1: \sigma^2 \neq 0.04$

Critical region <5.629 and >26.119

Test statistic $= \frac{(n-1)s^2}{\sigma^2} = \frac{14 \times 0.0006977}{0.04}$

$= 0.244$

This is in the critical region.

There is evidence that the variance is not 0.04

6 a $s^2 = 0.06125$ **b** $\bar{x} = 4.3125$

$H_0: \mu = 4.11 \quad H_1: \mu > 4.11$

Critical region > 1.895

Test statistic $= \frac{\bar{x} - \mu}{\frac{s}{\sqrt{n}}} = \frac{4.3125 - 4.11}{\frac{\sqrt{0.06125}}{\sqrt{8}}} = 2.3143$

The test statistic is in the critical region.

The mean weight is > 4.11

c $H_0: \sigma^2 = 0.19 \quad H_1: \sigma^2 \neq 0.19$

Critical region <2.167 and >14.067

Test statistic $= \frac{(n-1)s^2}{\sigma^2} = \frac{7 \times 0.06125}{0.19} = 2.256$

The test statistic is not in the critical region.

There is no evidence that σ^2 does not = 0.19

7 a $H_0: \sigma^2 = 110.25 \quad H_1: \sigma^2 < 110.25$

Critical region <10.117

Test statistic $= \frac{(n-1)s^2}{\sigma^2} = \frac{19 \times 8.5^2}{110.25} = 12.451$

The test statistic is not in the not critical region.

There is no evidence that the variance has reduced.

b Take a larger sample before committing to new component.

Mixed exercise 2F

1 $H_0: \mu = 28 \quad H_1: \mu \neq 28$

Critical region <-2.160 or > 2.160

Test statistic $= \frac{\bar{x} - \mu}{\frac{s}{\sqrt{n}}} = \frac{30.4 - 28}{\frac{6}{\sqrt{14}}} = 1.4967$

The test statistic is not in the critical region.

There is no evidence to suggest that μ does not = 28

2 $H_0: \mu = 10 \quad H_1: \mu > 10$

Critical region > 1.895

$\bar{x} = \frac{85}{8} = 10.625$

$s^2 = \frac{\sum x^2 - n\bar{x}^2}{n-1} = \frac{970.25 - 8 \times 10.625^2}{7} = 9.589...$

Test statistic $= \frac{\bar{x} - \mu}{\frac{s}{\sqrt{n}}} = \frac{10.625 - 10}{\sqrt{\frac{9.589...}{8}}}$

$= 0.571$ – not critical – no evidence to suggest that $\mu > 10$

3 $\bar{x} = 52.833...$ $s = 1.722....$

a Confidence interval

$= \left(\bar{x} - t_{n-1}\left(\frac{\alpha}{2}\right) \times \frac{s}{\sqrt{n}}, \bar{x} + t_{n-1}\left(\frac{\alpha}{2}\right)\right)$

$= \left(52.833... - 2.571 \times \frac{1.722...}{\sqrt{6}}, 52.833... + 2.571 \times \frac{1.722...}{\sqrt{6}}\right)$

$= (51.025, 54.641)$

b Confidence interval $= \left(\frac{(n-1)s^2}{\chi^2_{n-1}\left(\frac{\alpha}{2}\right)}, \frac{(n-1)s^2}{\chi^2_{n-1}\left(1 - \frac{\alpha}{2}\right)}\right)$

$= \left(\frac{5 \times 1.722...^2}{12.832}, \frac{5 \times 1.722...^2}{0.831}\right)$

$= (1.156, 17.850)$

c They are normally distributed.

4 a Confidence interval

$= \left(\bar{x} - t_{n-1}\left(\frac{\alpha}{2}\right) \times \frac{s}{\sqrt{n}}, \bar{x} + t_{n-1}\left(\frac{\alpha}{2}\right)\right)$

$= \left(9.8... - 2.110 \times \frac{0.7}{\sqrt{18}}, 9.8 + 2.110 \times \frac{0.7}{\sqrt{18}}\right)$

$= (9.451, 10.148)$

b Confidence interval $= \left(\frac{(n-1)s^2}{\chi^2_{n-1}\left(\frac{\alpha}{2}\right)}, \frac{(n-1)s^2}{\chi^2_{n-1}\left(1 - \frac{\alpha}{2}\right)}\right)$

$= \left(\frac{17 \times 0.49}{30.191}, \frac{17 \times 0.49}{7.564}\right)$

$= (0.276, 1.101)$

5 a Confidence interval $= \left(\frac{(n-1)s^2}{\chi^2_{n-1}\left(\frac{\alpha}{2}\right)}, \frac{(n-1)s^2}{\chi^2_{n-1}\left(1 - \frac{\alpha}{2}\right)}\right)$

$= \left(\frac{13 \times 1.8}{24.736}, \frac{13 \times 1.8}{5.009}\right)$

$= (0.946, 4.672)$

b Confidence interval $= \left(\frac{(n-1)s^2}{\chi^2_{n-1}\left(\frac{\alpha}{2}\right)}, \frac{(n-1)s^2}{\chi^2_{n-1}\left(1 - \frac{\alpha}{2}\right)}\right)$

$= \left(\frac{13 \times 1.8}{22.362}, \frac{13 \times 1.8}{5.892}\right)$

$= (1.046, 3.971)$

6 $\bar{x} = 20.95$ $s = 2.674...$

$H_0 : \mu = 21.5$ $H_1 : \mu < 21.5$

critical region < -1.895,

Test statistic $t = \frac{\bar{x} - \mu}{\frac{s}{\sqrt{n}}} = \frac{20.95 - 21.5...}{\frac{2.674...}{\sqrt{8}}} = -0.5817.$

The test statistic is not in the critical region.

There is no evidence to reject claim.

7 $\bar{x} = 6.1916....$ $s = 0.7549...$ $s^2 = 0.5699...$

a Confidence interval

$= \left(\bar{x} - t_{n-1}\left(\frac{\alpha}{2}\right) \times \frac{s}{\sqrt{n}}, \bar{x} + t_{n-1}\left(\frac{\alpha}{2}\right)\right)$

$= \left(6.1916... - 2.201 \times \frac{0.7549...}{\sqrt{12}}, 6.1916... + 2.201 \times \frac{0.7549...}{\sqrt{12}}\right)$

$= (5.712, 6.671)$

b Confidence interval Var. $= \left(\frac{(n-1)s^2}{\chi^2_{n-1}\left(\frac{\alpha}{2}\right)}, \frac{(n-1)s^2}{\chi^2_{n-1}\left(1 - \frac{\alpha}{2}\right)}\right)$

$= \left(\frac{11 \times 0.5699...}{21.920}, \frac{11 \times 0.5699}{3.816}\right)$

$= (0.286, 1.643)$

Confidence interval s.d. $= (0.535, 1.28)$

c He should measure his blood glucose at the same time each day.

8 $\bar{x} = \frac{1428}{20} = 71.4$ $s^2 = \frac{102\,286 - 20 \times 71.4^2}{19} = 17.2$

a Confidence interval $= \left(\frac{(n-1)s^2}{\chi^2_{n-1}\left(\frac{\alpha}{2}\right)}, \frac{(n-1)s^2}{\chi^2_{n-1}\left(1 - \frac{\alpha}{2}\right)}\right)$

$= \left(\frac{19 \times 17.2}{32.852}, \frac{19 \times 17.2}{8.907}\right)$

$= (9.948, 36.69)$

b $10 = 1.6449$ so $\sigma = \frac{10}{1.6449} = 6.079$

c $\sqrt{36.69} < 6.079$ the supervisor should not be concerned.

9 $\bar{x} = 11.5$ $s = 2.073...$

a Confidence interval

$= \left(\bar{x} - t_{n-1}\left(\frac{\alpha}{2}\right) \times \frac{s}{\sqrt{n}}, \bar{x} + t_{n-1}\left(\frac{\alpha}{2}\right)\right)$

$= \left(11.5 - 2.571 \times \frac{2.073...}{\sqrt{6}}, 11.5 + 2.571 \times \frac{2.073...}{\sqrt{6}}\right)$

$= (9.324, 13.675)$

b Confidence interval $= \left(\frac{(n-1)s^2}{\chi^2_{n-1}\left(\frac{\alpha}{2}\right)}, \frac{(n-1)s^2}{\chi^2_{n-1}\left(1 - \frac{\alpha}{2}\right)}\right)$

$= \left(\frac{5 \times 2.073...^2}{12.832}, \frac{5 \times 2.073...^2}{0.831}\right)$

$= (1.675, 25.872)$

10 a $H_0 : \sigma = 4$ $H_1 : \sigma > 4$

Critical region $\chi^2 > 16.919$

Test statistic $= \frac{(n-1)s^2}{\sigma^2} = \frac{9 \times 5.2^2}{4^2} = 15.21$

The test statistic is not in the critical region.

standard deviation = 4 months

b $H_0 : \mu = 24$ $H_1 : \mu > 24$

Critical region $t > 1.833$

Test statistic $t = \frac{\bar{x} - \mu}{\frac{s}{\sqrt{n}}} = \frac{27.2 - 24}{\frac{5.2}{\sqrt{10}}} = 1.946$

There is evidence to reject H_0

The mean battery life >24

c Lifetime is normally distributed.

11 $\bar{x} = 721.5$ $s = 10.399....$

a Confidence interval

$= \left(\bar{x} - t_{n-1}\left(\frac{\alpha}{2}\right) \times \frac{s}{\sqrt{n}}, \bar{x} + t_{n-1}\left(\frac{\alpha}{2}\right)\right)$

$= \left(721.5 - 2.093 \times \frac{10.399...}{\sqrt{20}}, 721.5 + 2.093 \times \frac{10.399...}{\sqrt{20}}\right)$

$= (717, 726)$

b Confidence interval variance

$= \left(\frac{(n-1)s^2}{\chi^2_{n-1}\left(\frac{\alpha}{2}\right)}, \frac{(n-1)s^2}{\chi^2_{n-1}\left(1 - \frac{\alpha}{2}\right)}\right)$

$= \left(\frac{19 \times 10.399...^2}{32.852}, \frac{19 \times 10.399...^2}{8.907}\right)$

$= (62.553, 230.717)$

Confidence interval standard deviation = (7.909, 15.189)

c 725 within confidence interval, There is no evidence to reject this hypothesis.

12 $\bar{x} = 45.1 \quad s = 6.838...$

$H_0 : \sigma = 5 \quad H_1 : \sigma \neq 5$

a Critical region > 19.023 and < 2.700

$$\text{Test statistic} = \frac{(n-1)s^2}{\sigma^2} = \frac{9 \times 6.838...^2}{5^2} = 16.836$$

There is insufficient evidence to reject H_0

$\sigma = 5$

b Critical region $z > 1.6449$

$$\text{Test statistic } z = \frac{X - \mu}{\frac{\sigma}{\sqrt{n}}} = \frac{45.1 - 40}{\frac{5}{\sqrt{10}}} = 3.225$$

The test statistic is in the critical region. There is evidence to suggest there is an increase in breaking strain.

c In **a** there was no change in σ so assume $\sigma = 5 \quad \therefore$ use z not t

13 **a** $\bar{x} = \frac{34.2}{10} = 3.42$

$$s^2 = \frac{\sum x^2 - n\bar{x}^2}{n-1} = \frac{121.6 - 10 \times 3.42^2}{9} = 0.5151...$$

b **i** Confidence interval mean

$$= \left(\bar{x} - t_{n-1}\left(\frac{\alpha}{2}\right) \times \frac{s}{\sqrt{n}}, \bar{x} + t_{n-1}\left(\frac{\alpha}{2}\right) \times \frac{s}{\sqrt{n}}\right)$$

$$= \left(3.42 - 2.262 \times \frac{0.7177...}{\sqrt{10}}, 3.42 + 2.262 \times \frac{0.7177...}{\sqrt{10}}\right)$$

$= (2.906, 3.933)$

ii Confidence interval variance

$$= \left(\frac{(n-1)s^2}{\chi_9^2(0.025)}, \frac{(n-1)s^2}{\chi_9^2(0.975)}\right)$$

$$= \left(\frac{9 \times 0.515...}{19.023}, \frac{9 \times 0.515...}{2.700}\right)$$

$= (0.244, 1.717)$

Confidence interval standard deviation = (0.4937, 1.3103)

c 3.5 hours is inside the confidence interval on the mean, so there is no evidence of a change in the mean time.

0.5 hours is inside the confidence interval on the standard deviation so there is no evidence of a change in the variability of the time.

There is no reason to change the repair method.

d Use a 'matched pairs' experiment, getting each engineer to carry out a similar repair using the old method and the new method and use a paired t-test.

Review exercise 1

1 $H_0 : \mu = 1012 \quad H_1 : \mu \neq 1012$

$$\bar{x} = \frac{13\,700}{14} (= 978.57...)$$

$$S_x^2 = \frac{13\,448\,750 - 14\bar{x}^2}{13} (= 3255.49)$$

$$t_{13} = \frac{\bar{x} - \mu}{\frac{s}{\sqrt{n}}} = \frac{978.6 - 1012}{\frac{57.06}{\sqrt{14}}} = -2.19...$$

$t_{13}(5\%)$ two-tail critical value $= -2.160$

Significant result – there is evidence of a change in mean weight of squirrels.

2 **a** $E(\theta_1) = \frac{E(X_3 + E(X_4) + E(X_5))}{3} = \frac{3\mu}{3} = \mu \quad \text{Bias} = 0$

$$E(\theta_2) = \frac{E(X_{10}) - E(X_1)}{3} = \frac{1}{3}(\mu - \mu) = 0 \quad \text{Bias} = -\mu$$

$$E(\theta_3) = \frac{3E(X_1) + 2E(X_2) + E(X_{10})}{6} = \frac{3\mu + 2\mu + \mu}{6} = \mu \quad \text{Bias} = 0$$

b $\text{Var}(\theta_1) = \frac{1}{9}(\sigma^2 + \sigma^2 + \sigma^2) = \frac{\sigma^2}{3}$

$$\text{Var}(\theta_2) = \frac{1}{9}(\sigma^2 + \sigma^2) = \frac{2\sigma^2}{9}$$

$$\text{Var}(\theta_3) = \frac{1}{36}(9\sigma^2 + 4\sigma^2 + \sigma^2) = \frac{14\sigma^2}{36} = \frac{7\sigma^2}{18}$$

c **ii** Don't use θ_2 as it is biased.

$$\text{Var}(\theta_1) = \frac{\sigma^2}{3} = \frac{6\sigma^2}{18}$$

$$\text{Var}(\theta_3) = \frac{\sigma^2}{18}$$

i So choose θ_i as it is unbiased and has the smallest variance to be the best estimator.

3 $H_0 : \mu = 5.1 \quad H_1 : \mu < 5.1$

$v = 9$

Critical Region $t < -2.262$

$\bar{x} = 4.91$

$$s^2 = \frac{241.89 - 10 \times (4.91)^2}{9} = 0.0899$$

$s = 0.300$

$$t = \frac{4.91 - 5.1}{\frac{0.3}{\sqrt{10}}} = -2.00$$

There is no evidence to suggest that the mean height is less than those grown previously.

4 $H_0 : \sigma = 4; \quad H_1 : \sigma > 4$

$v = 19, X_{19}^2(0.05) = 30.144$

$$\frac{(n-1)S^2}{\sigma^2} = \frac{19 \times 6.25}{4} = 29.6875$$

Since $29.68785 < 30.144$ there is insufficient evidence to reject H_0. There is insufficient evidence to suggest that the standard deviation is greater than 2

5 **a** $E(\bar{X}) = \mu$

$$\text{Var}(\bar{X}) = \text{Var}\left(\frac{X_1 + X_2 + X_3 + ... + X_n}{n}\right) = \frac{\sigma^2}{n}$$

d $\frac{n\bar{X} + m\bar{Y}}{n + m}$ is a better estimate since variance is smaller.

6 Let x represent weight of flour

$\sum x = 8055 \quad \therefore \bar{x} = 1006.875$

$$\sum x^2 = 8\,110\,611 \quad \therefore s^2 = \frac{1}{7}\left\{8\,110\,611 - \frac{8055^2}{8}\right\}$$

$= 33.26785...$

$\therefore s = 5.767825$

$H_0 : \mu = 1010; \quad H_1 : \mu < 1010$

critical value: $t = -1.895$ so critical region $t < -1.895$

$$t = \frac{(1006.875 - 1010)}{\left(\frac{5.7678}{\sqrt{8}}\right)} = -1.5324$$

Since -1.53 is not in the critical region there is insufficient evidence to reject H_0.

The mean weight of flour delivered by the machine is 1010 g.

7 **a** $1 - 0.8891 = 0.1109$
c $1 - 0.5583 = 0.442$
$1 - 0.00281 = 0.997$
d The test is more discriminating (powerful) for the larger value of p.

8 **a** $P(X \leqslant c_1) \leqslant 0.05$; $P(X \leqslant 3 | \lambda = 8) = 0.0424 \Rightarrow X \leqslant 3$
$P(X \geqslant c_2) \leqslant 0.05$; $P(X \geqslant 14 | \lambda = 8) = 0.0342$
$P(X \geqslant 13 | \lambda = 8) = 0.0638 \Rightarrow X \geqslant 13$
$\therefore$ critical region is $\{X \leqslant 3\} \cup \{X \geqslant 13\}$
b **i** $P(4 \leqslant X \leqslant 12 | \lambda = 10) = P(X \leqslant 12) - P(X \leqslant 3)$
$= 0.7916 - 0.0103$
$= 0.7813$
ii Power $= 1 - 0.7813 = 0.2187$

9 **a** $H_0 : \sigma^2 = 0.9 \quad H_1 : \sigma^2 \neq 0.9$
$v = 19$
CR (Lower tail 10.117)
Upper tail 30.144

Test statistic $= \dfrac{19 \times 1.5}{0.9} = 31.6666$, significant

There is sufficient evidence that the variance of the length of spring is different to 0.9
b $H_0 : \mu = 100 \quad H_1 : \mu > 100$
$t_{19} = 1.328$ is the critical value

$$t = \frac{100.6 - 100}{\sqrt{\frac{1.5}{20}}} = 2.19$$

Significant. The mean length of spring is greater than 100

10 **a** $\bar{x} = 668.125 \quad s = 84.425$
$t_7(5\%) = 1.895$

Confidence limits $= 668.125 \pm \dfrac{1.895 \times 84.425}{\sqrt{8}}$

$= 611.6$ and 724.7
Confidence interval $= (612, 725)$
b Normal distribution
c £650 is within the confidence interval.
No need to worry.

11 **a** $E(A_1) = E(X_1)E(X_2) = \mu^2$

$A_2 = \bar{X}^2, \bar{X} \sim N\left(\mu, \dfrac{\sigma^2}{2}\right) \therefore E(\bar{X}^2) = E(A_2) = \mu^2 + \dfrac{\sigma^2}{2}$

b A_1 is unbiased, bias for A_2 is $\dfrac{\sigma^2}{2}$
c Used A_1 since it is unbiased
d $E(\bar{X}^2) = \mu^2 + \dfrac{\sigma^2}{n}$; as $n \to \infty$, $E(\bar{X}^2) \to \mu^2$

$\text{Var}(\bar{X}^2) = \dfrac{2\sigma^4}{n^2} + \dfrac{4\sigma^2\mu^2}{n}$; as $n \to \infty$, $\text{Var}(\bar{X}^2) \to 0$

$\bar{X}^2$ is a consistent estimator of μ^2

12 **a** $$s^2 = \frac{2962 - 15 \times \left(\frac{208}{15}\right)^2}{14} = 5.55$$

or $(n - 1)s^2 = 2962 - \dfrac{208^2}{15} = 77.3$

$$\frac{14 \times 5.55}{23.685} < \sigma^2 < \frac{14 \times 5.55}{6.571}$$

$3.28 < \sigma^2 < 11.83$
b Since 9 lies in the interval, yes

13 **a** Type I H_0 rejected when it is true
Type II – H_0 is accepted when it is false
b $H_0 : \lambda = 5 \quad H_1 : \lambda > 5$
$P(X \geqslant 7 | \lambda = 5) = 1 - 0.7622 = 0.2378 > 0.05$
No evidence of an increase in the number of chicks reared per year.
c $P(X \geqslant c | \lambda = 5) < 0.05$
$P(X \geqslant 9) = 0.0681$, $P(X \geqslant 10) = 0.0318$, $c = 10$
P(Type I Error) $= 0.0318$
d $\lambda = 8$
$P(X \leqslant 9 | \lambda = 8) = 0.7166$

14 **a** **i** $E(\hat{\theta}) = \theta$
ii $E(\hat{\theta}) = \theta$ or $E(\hat{\theta}) \to \theta$
and $\text{Var}(\hat{\theta}) \to 0$ as $n \to \infty$ where n is the sample size
b $E(\hat{p}_1) = p$, $\therefore$ Bias $= 0$

$E(\hat{p}_2) = \dfrac{5p}{6}$, Bias $= -\dfrac{1}{6}p$

$E(\hat{p}_3) = p$, $\therefore$ Bias $= 0$

c $\text{Var}(\hat{p}_1) = \dfrac{1}{9n^2}\{npq + npq + npq\}$

$= \dfrac{pq}{3n}$ or $\dfrac{12pq}{36n}$

$\text{Var}(\hat{p}_2) = \dfrac{1}{36n^2}\{npq + 9npq + npq\} = \dfrac{11pq}{36n}$

$\text{Var}(\hat{p}_3) = \dfrac{1}{36n^2}\{4npq + 9npq + npq\} = \dfrac{7pq}{18n}$ or $\dfrac{14pq}{36n}$

d **i** $\hat{p}_1$; unbiased and smallest variance
ii $\hat{p}_2$; biased

15 **a** A Type I error occurs when H_0 is rejected when it is in fact true.
b The size of a test is the probability of a type I error.
c $X \sim B(8, 0.25)$
Size $P(X > 6) = 1 - P(X \leqslant 6 | n = 8, p = 0.25)$
$= 1 - 0.9996 = 0.0004$
e Power $= 8 \times 0.3^7 - 7 \times 0.3^8$
$= 1 - 0.9996 = 0.0004$
f Power $= 1 -$ P(Type II)
P(Type II) $= 1 -$ power
$= 1 - 0.00129$
$= 0.9087...$
g Increase the probability of a Type I error, e.g. increase the significance level of the test.
Increase the value of p.

16 **a** $X_1 =$ number of defects in 15 m $\quad X_1 \sim Po(4.5)$
Size $= P(X_2 \geqslant 9) = 1 - 0.9597 = 0.0403$
b $r = P(X_2 \geqslant 9 | X_2 \sim Po(9)) = 1 - 0.4557 = 0.54(43)$
c $Y_1 =$ number of defects in 10 m $\quad Y_1 \sim Po(3)$
$P(Y_1 \geqslant c) < 0.10 \quad Y_1 \geqslant 6$
d Size $= P(Y_1 \geqslant 6) = 1 - P(Y_1 \leqslant 5)$
$= 1 - 0.9161 = 0.0839$
e $s = 1 - P(Y_2 \leqslant 5) = 1 - 0.1912 = 0.8088$
f

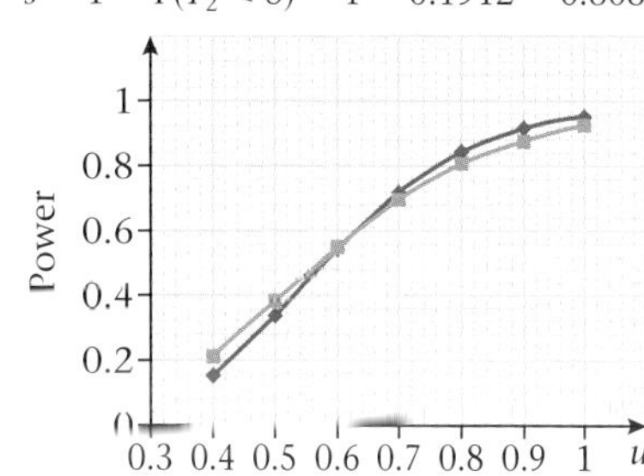

g **i** 0.62 to 0.67 **ii** Test I more powerful
h Test 2 has a higher P(type I error) but cost of this is low.

Test 2 is more powerful for $\lambda < 0.7$ and $\lambda > 0.7$ is rare.
Adopt Test 2.

17 a Power $= \mathrm{P}\left(X \leqslant \frac{3}{\lambda}\right)$

$= \mathrm{e}^{-\lambda} + \mathrm{e}^{-\lambda}\lambda + \frac{\mathrm{e}^{-\lambda}\lambda^2}{2} + \frac{\mathrm{e}^{-\lambda}\lambda^3}{6}$

$= \frac{\mathrm{e}^{-\lambda}}{6}(6 + 6\lambda + 3\lambda^2 + \lambda^3)$

b CR is $X \leqslant 3$

Size $= \mathrm{P}[X \leqslant 3 \mid \lambda = 7]$

$= 0.0818$

c P(Type II error) $= 1 -$ power

$= 1 - \frac{\mathrm{e}^{-4}}{6}(6 + 6 \times 4 + 3 \times 4^2 + 4^3)$

$= 0.5665...$

18 a 95% confidence interval for μ is

$1.68 \pm t_{24}(2.5\%)\sqrt{\frac{1.79}{25}} = 1.68 \pm 2.064\sqrt{\frac{1.79}{25}}$

$= (1.13, 2.23)$

b 95% confidence interval for σ^2 is

$12.401 < \frac{24 \times 1.79}{\sigma^2} < 39.364$

$\sigma^2 > 1.09, \sigma^2 < 3.46$

$\therefore$ CI on σ^2 is (1.09, 3.46)

c Require $\mathrm{P}(X > 2.5) = \mathrm{P}\left(Z > \frac{2.5 - \mu}{\sigma}\right)$ to be as small as possible OR $\frac{2.5 - \mu}{\sigma}$ to be as large as possible;

both imply lowest σ and μ.

$\frac{2.5 - 1.13}{\sqrt{1.09}} = 1.31$

$\mathrm{P}(Z > 1.31) = 1 - 0.9049 = 0.0951$

19 c Minimum value when $(4a - 2)\sigma^2 = 0$

$\Rightarrow 4a - 2 = 0$

$a = \frac{1}{2}, b = \frac{1}{2}$

20 a $\bar{x} = 123.1$

$s = 5.87745...$

(NB: $\sum x = 1231$; $\sum x^2 = 151\,847$)

i 95% confidence interval is given by

$123.1 \pm 2.262 \times \frac{5.87745...}{\sqrt{10}}$

i.e. (118.8958..., 127.30418...)

ii 95% confidence interval is given by

$\frac{9 \times 5.87745...^2}{19.023} < \sigma^2 < \frac{9 \times 5.87745...^2}{2.700}$

i.e. (16.34336..., 115.14806...)

b 130 is just above confidence interval
16 is just above confidence interval
Thus supervisor should be concerned about the speed of the new typist since both their average speed is too slow and the variability of the time is too large.

21 a Confidence interval $= \left(\frac{15 \times 0.003}{27.488}, \frac{15 \times 0.003}{6.262}\right)$

$= (0.00164, 0.00719)$

b $0.07^2 = 0.0049$
0.0049 is within the 95% confidence interval.
There is no evidence to reject the idea that the standard deviation of the volumes is not 0.07 or the machine is working well.

22 a $\frac{\bar{X} - 250}{\frac{4}{\sqrt{15}}} > 2.3263$ or $\frac{\bar{X} - 250}{\frac{4}{\sqrt{15}}} < -2.3263$

$\bar{X} > 252.40...$ or $\bar{X} < 247.6...$

b $\mathrm{P}(\bar{X} < 252.4 \mid \mu = 254) - \mathrm{P}(\bar{X} < 247.6 \mid \mu = 254)$

$= \mathrm{P}\left(Z < \frac{252.4 - 254}{\frac{4}{\sqrt{15}}}\right) - \mathrm{P}\left(Z < \frac{247.6 - 254}{\frac{4}{\sqrt{15}}}\right)$

$= \mathrm{P}(Z < -1.5492) - \mathrm{P}(Z < -6.20)$

$= (1 - 0.9394) - (1 - 1)$

$= 0.0606$

23 a $\mathrm{H}_0 : p = 0.35 \quad \mathrm{H}_1 : p \neq 0.35$

b Let X = Number cured then $X \sim \mathrm{B}(20, 0.35)$

α = P(Type I error) $= \mathrm{P}(x \leqslant 3) + \mathrm{P}(x \geqslant 11)$ given $p = 0.35$

$= 0.0444 + 0.0532$

$= 0.0976$

c β = P(Type II error) $= \mathrm{P}(4 \leqslant x \leqslant 10)$

p	0.2	0.3	0.4	0.5
β	0.5880	0.8758	0.8565	0.5868

d Power $= 1 - \beta$

0.4120 0.1435

e Not a good procedure.
Better further away from 0.35 or
this is not a very powerful test (power $= 1 - \beta$)

24 $\bar{x} = 4.01$

$s = 0.7992...$

a $4.01 \pm t_9\,(2.5\%)\frac{0.7992...}{\sqrt{10}} = 4.01 \pm 2.262\frac{0.7992...}{\sqrt{10}}$

$= 4.5816...$ and $3.4383...$

i.e. (3.4383, 4.5816)

b $2.700 < \frac{9 \times 0.7992...^2}{s^2} < 19.023$

$\sigma^2 < 2.13, \sigma^2 > 0.302$ i.e. (0.302, 2.13)

c $\mathrm{P}(X > 7) = \mathrm{P}Z > \left(\frac{7 - \mu}{\sigma}\right)$ needs to be as high as possible.

Therefore μ and σ must be as big as possible.

Proportion with high blood glucose level

$= \mathrm{P}\left(Z > \frac{7 - 4.581}{\sqrt{2.13}}\right)$

$= 1 - 0.9515$

$= 0.0485$

$= 4.85\%$

Exercise 3A

1 a 2.34 **b** 3.36 **c** 3.37

2 a $\frac{1}{F_{8,6}} = 0.241$ **b** $\frac{1}{F_{12,25}} = 0.463$ **c** $\frac{1}{F_{5,5}} = 0.198$

3 a 3.37 **b** 4.20 **c** 6.06

4 a $\frac{1}{F_{12,3}} = 0.0370$ **b** $\frac{1}{F_{12,8}} = 0.176$ **c** $\frac{1}{F_{12,5}} = 0.101$

5 a $3.07, \frac{1}{F_{10,8}} = 0.299$ **b** $2.91, \frac{1}{F_{10,12}} = 0.364$

c $5.41, \frac{1}{F_{5,3}} = 0.111$

6 a $\mathrm{P}(X < 0.5) = \mathrm{P}(F_{40,12} < 0.5)$

$= \mathrm{P}\left(F_{12,40} > \frac{1}{0.5}\right)$

$= \mathrm{P}(F_{12,40} > 2)$

From the tables $F_{12,40}(0.05) = 2$

$\therefore P(F_{12,40} > 2) = P(F_{40,12} < 0.5) = 0.05$

7 $P(X < 3.28) = 1 - P(F_{12,8} > 3.28)$
$= 1 - 0.05 = 0.95$

$$P\left(X < \frac{1}{2.85}\right) = P\left(F_{12,8} < \frac{1}{2.85}\right)$$
$$= P(F_{8,12} > 2.85)$$

$$\therefore P\left(X < \frac{1}{2.85}\right) = 0.05$$

$$P\left(\frac{1}{2.85} < X < 5.06\right) = P(X < 5.06) - P\left(X < \frac{1}{2.85}\right)$$
$$= 0.95 - 0.05$$
$$= 0.90$$

8 $P(X < 9.55) = 1 - P(F_{2,7} > 9.55)$
$= 1 - 0.01$
$= 0.99$

9 b ${}^6C_2(0.9)^2(0.1)^4 \times 0.9 = 0.00109$

Exercise 3B

1 Critical value is $F_{10,6} = 4.06$

$$F_{\text{test}} = \frac{7.6}{6.4} = 1.1875$$

not in critical region
accept H_0 – there is evidence to suggest that $\sigma_1^2 = \sigma_2^2$

2 Critical value is $F_{24,40} = 2.29$

$$F_{\text{test}} = \frac{0.42}{0.17} = 2.4706$$

In critical region
reject H_0 – there is evidence to suggest that $\sigma_1^2 > \sigma_2^2$

3 a Critical value is $F_{12,8} = 3.28$

$$F_{\text{test}} = \frac{225}{63} = 3.57$$

In critical region
reject H_0 – there is evidence to suggest that the machines differ in variability

b Population distributions are assumed to be normal

4 Critical value is $F_{8,12} = 2.85$

$$F_{\text{test}} = \frac{52.6}{36.4} = 1.445$$

not in critical region
accept H_0 – there is evidence to suggest that $\sigma_1^2 = \sigma_2^2$

5 a $\sigma_{\text{Goodstick}}^2 = 1.363$
$\sigma_{\text{Holdtight}}^2 = 0.24167$
Critical value is $F_{4,5} = 5.19$

$$F_{\text{test}} = \frac{1.363}{0.24167} = 5.64$$

In critical region
reject H_0 – there is evidence to suggest that the variances are not equal.

b Holdtight as it is less variable and cheaper.

6 $\sigma_{\text{Chegrit}}^2 = 22\,143.286$
$\sigma_{\text{Dicabalk}}^2 = 6570.85238$
Critical value is $F_{6,14} = 2.85$

$$F_{\text{test}} = \frac{22\,143.286}{6570.85238} = 3.3699$$

In critical region – there is evidence to suggest that their variances differ.

7 a $\mu_1 = 1046$ $s_2^1 = 1818.11$ and $\mu_2 = 997.75$ $s_2^2 = 1200.21$

b Critical value is $F_{8,7} = 3.73$

$$F_{\text{test}} = \frac{1818.111}{1200.21} = 1.5148$$

not in critical region
accept H_0 – there is evidence to suggest that $\sigma_1^2 = \sigma_2^2$

c Use present supplier who appears to have a higher mean.

Exercise 3C

1 a $$s_p^2 = \frac{(9 \times 4) + (14 \times 5.3)}{10 + 15 - 2} = 4.7913$$

$s_p = 2.189$
$t_{23}(2.5\%) = 2.069$

$$(25 - 22) \pm 2.069 \times 2.189\sqrt{\tfrac{1}{15} + \tfrac{1}{10}} = 3 \pm 1.849$$
$$= (1.151, 4.849)$$

b Independent random samples, normal distributions, common variance

2 $\bar{x}_s = 8.9125$ $\quad s_s^2 = 0.58125$
$\bar{x}_{ns} = 12.04$ $\quad s_{ns}^2 = 0.84933$

$$s_p^2 = \frac{(7 \times 0.58125) + (9 \times 0.849)}{10 + 8 - 2} = 0.7319$$

$s_p = 0.8555$
$t_{16}(5\%) = 1.746$

$$(12.04 - 8.9125) \pm 1.746 \times 0.855\sqrt{\tfrac{1}{10} + \tfrac{1}{8}}$$
$$= 3.1275 \pm 0.7081 = (2.419, 3.836)$$

3 a $$s_p^2 = \frac{(19 \times 6.1^2) + (19 \times 5.2^2)}{20 + 20 - 2} = 32.125$$

$s_p = 5.66789$
$t_{38}(0.5\%) = 2.712$

$$(38.2 - 32.7) \pm 2.712 \times 5.66789\sqrt{\tfrac{1}{20} + \tfrac{1}{20}}$$
$$= 5.5 \pm 4.86083 = (0.6392, 10.3608)$$

b normality and equal variances

c zero not in interval $\Rightarrow$ method B seems better than method A

4 Assume same variances,

$$s_p^2 = \frac{(9 \times 32.488) + (9 \times 33.344)}{10 + 10 - 2} = 32.916$$

$s_p = 5.73725$
$t_{18}(5\%) = 1.734$

$$(18.6 - 14.3) \pm 1.734 \times 5.73725\sqrt{\tfrac{1}{10} + \tfrac{1}{10}}$$
$$= 4.3 \pm 4.44905 = (-0.149, 8.749)$$

Exercise 3D

1 a $$s_p^2 = \frac{(19 \times 12) + (10 \times 12)}{20 + 11 - 2} = 12$$

b $H_0 : \mu_{1st} = \mu_{2nd}$ $\quad H_1 : \mu_{1st} \neq \mu_{2nd}$
critical value $t_{29}(0.025) = 2.045$
critical region is $t \leqslant -2.045$ and $t \geqslant 2.045$

$$t = \frac{(16 - 14) - 0}{3.464\sqrt{\tfrac{1}{20} + \tfrac{1}{11}}} = 1.538$$

Not in critical region – do not reject H_0.
There is evidence to suggest that the populations have the same mean.

2 $H_0 : \mu_F = \mu_c$ $\quad H_1 : \mu_F > \mu_c$
$\bar{x}_w = 38.67,$ $\quad s_w^2 = 5.5827$
$\bar{x}_c = 41.625,$ $\quad s_c^2 = 1.5625$

$$s_p^2 = \frac{(5 \times 5.5827) + (3 \times 1.5625)}{6 + 4 - 2} = 4.075$$

critical value $t_8(0.05) = 1.86$
critical region is $t \geqslant 1.860$

$$t = \frac{(41.625 - 38.67) - 0}{2.0187\sqrt{\frac{1}{6} + \frac{1}{4}}} = 2.270$$

In the critical region – reject H_0.
There is evidence to suggest that the salmon are wild.

3 **a** $\bar{x}_t = 0.1185$ $s_t^2 = 0.0005227$

$\bar{x}_e = 0.1425$ $s_e^2 = 0.0011319$

$$s_p^2 = \frac{(5 \times 0.0005227) + (5 \times 0.0011319)}{6 + 6 - 2} = 0.000827$$

$H_0 : \mu_t = \mu_e$ $H_1 : \mu_t \neq \mu_e$
critical value $t_{10}(0.025) = 2.228$
critical region $t \leqslant 2.228$ and $t \geqslant 2.228$

$$t = \frac{(0.1425 - 0.1185) - 0}{0.02876\sqrt{\frac{1}{6} + \frac{1}{6}}} = 1.445$$

Not in the critical region – accept H_0.
There is evidence to suggest that Tetracycline and Erythromycin are equally as effective.

b $\bar{x}_s = 0.2387$ $s_s^2 = 0.0004959$

$\bar{x}_2 = 0.1305$ $s_2^2 = 0.000909$

$$s_p^2 = \frac{(11 \times 0.000909) + (5 \times 0.0004959)}{12 + 6 - 2} = 0.000780$$

$H_0 : \mu_s = \mu_2$ $H_1 : \mu_s \neq \mu_2$
critical value $t_{16}(0.05) = 1.746$
critical region $t \geqslant 1.746$

$$t = \frac{(0.2387 - 0.1305) - 0}{0.0279\sqrt{\frac{1}{12} + \frac{1}{6}}} = 7.75$$

In the critical region – reject H_0.
There is evidence to suggest that Streptomycin is more effective than the others.

4 **a** $H_0 : \mu_{\text{old}} = \mu_{\text{new}}$ $H_1 : \mu_{\text{old}} > \mu_{\text{new}}$

b $\bar{x}_{old} = 7.911$ $s_{old}^2 = 5.206$

$\bar{x}_{new} = 5.9$ $s_{new}^2 = 3.98$

$$s_p^2 = \frac{(6 \times 3.98) + (8 \times 5.206)}{7 + 9 - 2} = 4.6806$$

critical value $t_{14} = 1.761$
critical region $t \geqslant 1.761$

$$\text{Test statistic } t = \frac{(7.911 - 5.9) - 0}{2.1635\sqrt{\frac{1}{9} + \frac{1}{7}}} = 1.8446$$

Significant – there is evidence to suggest that new language does improve time.

c Once task is solved the programmer should be quicker next time with either language.

5 **b** $\bar{x}_v = 32$ $s_v^2 = 17.45$

$\bar{x}_s = 35.6$ $s_s^2 = 22.829$

$$s_p^2 = \frac{(14 \times 22.829) + (11 \times 17.45)}{12 + 15 - 2} = 20.464$$

c $H_0 : \mu_v = \mu_s$ $H_1 : \mu_v \neq \mu_s$
critical value $t_{25}(0.025) = 2.060$
critical region $t \leqslant -2.060$ and $t \leqslant 2.060$

$$t = \frac{(35.6 - 32) - 0}{4.524\sqrt{\frac{1}{15} + \frac{1}{12}}} = 2.0547 \text{ – accept } H_0$$

– no evidence to suggest difference in means

d normality

e same types of driving, roads and weather.

Exercise 3E

1 **a** **i** $H_0 : \mu_D = 0$ $H_1 : \mu_D \neq 0$

ii $H_0 : \mu_D = 0$ $H_1 : \mu_D > 0$

b $\sum d = 30$ $\sum d^2 = 238$

$\bar{d} = 5$

$$s^2 = \frac{238 - 6(5)^2}{5} = 17.6$$

$s = 4.195$
Critical value $t_5(5\%) = 2.015$
The critical region is $t > 2.015$

$$t = \frac{5 - 0}{\frac{4.195}{\sqrt{6}}}$$

$= 2.919$
In the critical region, reject H_0.
There is evidence to suggest that there has been an increase in shorthand speed.

2 $H_0 : \mu_D = 0$ $H_1 : \mu_D > 0$

$\sum d = 5$ $\sum d^2 = 59$

$\bar{d} = 0.5$

$$s^2 = \frac{59 - 10(0.5)^2}{9} = 6.278$$

$s = 2.50555$
Critical value $t_9(1\%) = 2.821$
The critical region is $t > 2.821$

$$t = \frac{0.5 - 0}{\frac{2.50555}{\sqrt{10}}}$$

$= 0.631$
Not in the critical region. Do not reject H_0.
There is evidence to suggest that paper 2 is easier than paper 1.

3 **a** $H_0 : \mu_D = 0$ $H_1 : \mu_D > 0$

$\sum d = 47$ $\sum d^2 = 315$

$\bar{d} = 4.7$

$$s^2 = \frac{315 - 10(4.7)^2}{9} = 10.456$$

$s = 3.234$
Critical value $t_9(5\%) = 1.833$
The critical region is $t > 1.833$

$$t = \frac{4.7 - 0}{\frac{3.234}{\sqrt{10}}}$$

$= 4.596$
In the critical region. Reject H_0.
There is evidence to suggest that chewing the gum does not reduce the craving for cigarettes.

b The differences are normally distributed.

4 $H_0 : \mu_D = 0$ $H_1 : \mu_D > 0$

$\sum d = 46$ $\sum d^2 = 336$

$\bar{d} = 4.6$

$$s^2 = \frac{336 - 10(4.6)^2}{9} = 13.8222$$

$s = 3.7178$
Critical value $t_9(5\%) = 1.833$
The critical region is $t > 1.833$.

$$t = \frac{4.6 - 0}{\frac{3.7178}{\sqrt{10}}}$$

$= 3.913$

In the critical region. Reject H_0. There is evidence to suggest that the journey times have decreased.

5 **a** $H_0 : \mu_D = 0 \quad H_1 : \mu_D \neq 0$

$\sum d = 20 \quad \sum d^2 = 604$

$\bar{d} = 2.5$

$$s^2 = \frac{604 - 8(2.5)^2}{7} = 79.1429$$

$s = 8.896$

Critical value $t_7(5\%) = 1.895$

The critical regions are $t > -1.895$ and $t > 1.895$

$$t = \frac{2.5 - 0}{\frac{8.896}{\sqrt{8}}}$$

$= 0.795$

Not in the critical region. Do not reject H_0.

The mock examination is a good predictor.

b The differences are normally distributed.

6 **a** Different people will have differnt productivity rates. Need a common link if want to compare before and after. This reduces experimental error due to differences between individuals so that, if a difference does exist, it is more likely to be detected.

b $H_0 : \mu_D = 0 \quad H_1 : \mu_D > 0$

$\sum d = 65 \quad \sum d^2 = 569$

$\bar{d} = 6.5$

$$s^2 = \frac{569 - 10(6.5)^2}{9} = 16.278$$

$s = 4.0346$

Critical value $t_9(5\%) = 1.833$

The critical region is $t > 1.833$

$$t = \frac{6.5 - 0}{\frac{4.0346}{\sqrt{10}}}$$

$= 5.095$

In the critical region. Reject H_0.

There is evidence to suggest a tea break increases the number of garments made.

7 $H_0 : \mu_D = 0 \quad H_1 : \mu_D > 0$

$\sum d = 8.6 \quad \sum d^2 = 20.78$

$\bar{d} = 1.075$

$$s^2 = \frac{20.78 - 8(1.075)^2}{7} = 1.64786$$

$s = 1.2837$

Critical value $t_7(1\%) = 2.998$

The critical region is $t > 2.998$

$$t = \frac{1.075 - 0}{\frac{1.2827}{\sqrt{8}}}$$

$= 2.3686$

Not in the critical region. Do not reject H_0.

There is evidence to suggest that the drug increases the mean number of hours sleep per night.

Mixed exercise 3F

1 $P(F_{5,10} \geqslant 3.33) = 0.05 \Rightarrow b = 3.33$

$P(F_{10,5} \geqslant 4.47) = 0.05 \Rightarrow P\left(F_{5,10} \leqslant \frac{1}{4.74}\right) = 0.05$

$\therefore a = 0.2109$

2 d: 5, 13, −8, 2, −3, 4, 11, −1

$\left(\sum d = 23, \sum d^2 = 409\right) \quad \bar{d} = 2.875,\ sd = 6.9987\ (\approx 7.00)$

$H_0 : \mu_d = 0 \quad H_1 : \mu_d > 0$

$$t = \frac{(2.875 - 0)}{\frac{6.9987}{\sqrt{8}}} = 1.1618...\ (\approx 1.16)$$

Critical value $t_7(10\%) = 1.415$ (one-tailed)

Critical region is $t > 1.415$

Not significant

Insufficient evidence to support the chemist's claim

3 **a** $H_0 : \sigma_1^2 = \sigma_2^2;\ H_1 : \sigma_1^2 \neq \sigma_2^2$

$$\frac{s_1^2}{s_2^2} = \frac{14^2}{8^2} = \mathbf{3.0625} \text{ or } \frac{8^2}{14^2} = 0.32653...$$

C.V.: $F_{12,7} = 3.57 \qquad$ C.V.: $F_{7,12} = \frac{1}{3.57} = 0.28011$

Since 3.0625 is not in the critical region there is insufficient evidence to reject H_0. There is insufficient evidence of a difference in the variances of the lengths of the fence posts.

b The distribution of the population of lengths of fence posts is normally distributed.

4 **a** The data were not collected in pairs.

b Use data from twin lambs.

c Age, weight, gender

d $d = B - A$

d: 2, 1.2, 1, 1.8, −1, 2.2, 2, −1.2, 1.1, 2.8

$\sum d = 11.9;\ \sum d^2 = 30.01$

$\therefore\ \bar{d} = 1.19;\ s^2 = 1.761\ (s = 1.327)$

$H_0 : d = 0 \quad H_1 : d \neq 0 \qquad$ Allow μ_D for d

$$t = \frac{1.19 - 0}{\sqrt{\frac{1.761}{10}}} = 2.83574...$$

$\mu = 9$; C.V.: $t = 2.262$

Critical regions $t < -2.262$ or $t > 2.262$

Since 2.8357... is in the critical region ($t = 2.262$) there is evidence to reject H_0. The (mean) weight gained by the lambs is different for each diet.

e Diet B – it has the higher mean.

5 **a** d: 14, 2, 18, 25, 0, −8, 4, 4, 12, 20

$\left(\sum d = 91;\ \sum x^2 = 1789\right)$

$\therefore\ \bar{d} = 9.1 \quad s = \sqrt{106.7} = 10.332...$

$H_0 : \mu_d = 0 \quad H_1 : \mu_d \neq 0$

$$t = \frac{(9.1 - 0)}{\frac{10.332}{\sqrt{10}}} = 2.785$$

Critical value $t_9 = \pm 1.833$

critical regions $t \leqslant -1.833$ or $t \geqslant 1.833$

Significant. There is a difference between *blood pressure* measured by arm cuff and finger monitor.

b The *difference in measurements* of blood pressure is *normally* distributed.

6 **a** $H_0 : \sigma_F^2 = \sigma_M^2 \quad H_1 : \sigma_F^2 \neq \sigma_M^2$

$$s_F^2 = \frac{1}{6}(17\,956 - 7 \times 50.6^2) = \frac{33.98}{6} = 5.66333...$$

$$s_M^2 = \frac{1}{9}(28\,333.1 - 10 \times 53.2^2) = \frac{32.7}{6} = 3.63333...$$

$$\frac{s_F^2}{s_M^2} = 1.5587... \quad \text{(Reciprocal 0.6415)}$$

$F_{6,9} = 3.37$ (or 0.0297)

Not in critical region. There is no reason to doubt the *variances* of the two distributions *are the same.*

b $H_0 : \mu_F = \mu_M \quad H_1 : \mu_F < \mu_M$

Pooled estimate $s^2 = \dfrac{6 \times 5.66333... + 9 \times 3.63333}{15}$

$= 4.44533$

$s = 2.11$

$$t = \frac{50.6 - 53.2}{2.11\sqrt{\frac{1}{7} + \frac{1}{10}}} = 22.50$$

C.V.: $t_{15}(5\%) = -1.753$

so critical region $t \leqslant -1.753$

Significant. The mean length of the *females forewing* is less than the length of the males forewing.

7 Differences: 2.1, −0.7, 2.6, −1.7, 3.3, 1.6, 1.7, 1.2, 1.6, 2.4

$\sum d = 14.1 \quad \sum d^2 = 40.65 \quad d = 1.41$

$H_0 : \mu_d = 0 \quad H_1 : \mu_d > 0$

$$s = \sqrt{\frac{40.65 - 10 \times 1.41^2}{9}} = 1.5191...$$

$$t = \frac{1.41}{\left(\frac{1.519...}{\sqrt{10}}\right)} = 2.935$$

$t_9(1\%) = 2.821$

so critical region $t > 2.821$

$2.935... > 2.821$ Evidence to reject H_0.

There has been an increase in the mean weight of the mice.

8 **b** $H_0 : \sigma_o^2 = \sigma_n^2 \quad H_1 : \sigma_o^2 < \sigma_n^2$

critical value is $F_{8,9} = 3.23$

so critical region, $F \geqslant 3.23$

$$F_{\text{test}} = \frac{14.5}{8.2} = 1.768$$

not in critical region

accept H_0 – there is evidence to suggest that $\sigma_o^2 = \sigma_n^2$

c $$s_p^2 = \frac{(9 \times 8.2) + (8 \times 14.5)}{10 + 9 - 2} = 11.1647$$

$H_0 : \mu_o = \mu_n \quad H_1 : \mu_o \neq \mu_n$

critical value $t_{17}(0.01) = 2.567$

critical region $t \leqslant -2.567$ and $t \geqslant 2.567$

$$t = \frac{(26 - 22.5) - 0}{\sqrt{11.1647}\sqrt{\frac{1}{10} + \frac{1}{9}}} = 2.2798$$

Not in the critical region – do not reject H_0.

There is evidence to suggest that there is no difference in mean times between the old and new equipment.

d $t_{17}(2.5\%) = 2.110$

$$(26 - 22.5) \pm 2.110 \times \sqrt{11.1647} \times \sqrt{\frac{1}{10} + \frac{1}{9}}$$

$= 3.5 \pm 3.2394 = (0.261, 6.739)$

e Need to learn new equipment

f Gather data on new equipment after it has been mastered.

Review exercise 2

1 $F_{10,12}(5\%) = 2.75 \therefore b = 2.75$

$$a = \frac{1}{2.91} = 0.344$$

2 d: 7, 2, −3, 1, −1, −2, 10, 5

$\sum d = 19; \sum d^2 = 193$

$$\therefore \bar{d} = \frac{19}{8} = 2.375; s_d^2 = \frac{1}{7}\left\{193 - \frac{19^2}{8}\right\} = 21.125$$

$H_0 : \mu_D = 0; \quad H_1 : \mu_D > 0$

$$t = \frac{2.375 - 0}{\sqrt{\frac{21.125}{8}}} = 1.4615...$$

$v = 7 \Rightarrow$ critical region: $t > 1.895$

Since 1.4195... is *not* in the critical region there is insufficient evidence to reject H_0 and we conclude that there is insufficient evidence to support the doctors' belief.

3 **a** $H_0 : \sigma_G^2 = \sigma_B^2 \quad H_1 : \sigma_G^2 \neq \sigma_B^2$

$$s_B^2 = \frac{1}{6}(56\,130 - 7 \times 88.9^2) = \frac{807.53}{6} = 134.6$$

$$s_G^2 = \frac{1}{7}(55\,746 - 8 \times 83.1^2) = \frac{501.12}{7} = 71.58$$

$$\frac{s_B^2}{s_G^2} = 1.880...$$

critical value is $F_{6,7} = 3.87$

not significant, variances are the same

b $H_0 : \mu_B = \mu_G, \quad H_1 : \mu_B > \mu_G$

pooled estimate of variance

$$s^2 = \frac{6 \times 134.6 + 7 \times 71.58}{13} = 100.666153...$$

test statistic $t = \dfrac{88.9 - 83.1}{s\sqrt{\frac{1}{7} + \frac{1}{8}}} = 1.1169$

critical value $t_{13}(5\%) = 1.771$

Insufficient evidence to support parent's claim

4 **a** $$s_p^2 = \frac{7 \times 7.84 + 7 \times 4}{7 + 7} = 5.92$$

$s_p = 2.433105$

$H_0 : \mu_A = \mu_B, \quad H_1 : \mu_A > \mu_B$

$$t = \frac{26.125 - 25}{2.43\sqrt{\frac{1}{8} + \frac{1}{8}}} = 0.92474$$

$t_{14}(2.5\%) = 2.145$

Insufficient evidence to reject H_0.

Conclude that there is no difference in the means.

b $d = 2, 5, -2, 1, 3, -4, 1, 3$

$\bar{d} = \frac{9}{8} = 1.125$

$$s_d^2 = \frac{69 - 8 \times 1.125^2}{7} = 8.410714$$

$H_0 : \delta = 0, \quad H_1 : \delta \neq 0$

$$t = \frac{1.125}{\sqrt{\frac{8.41}{8}}} = 1.0972$$

$t_7(2.5\%) = 2.365$

There is no significant evidence of a difference between method A and method B.

c Paired sample as they are two measurements on the same orange.

5 $P(X > 2.85) = 0.05$

$$P\left(X < \frac{1}{5.67}\right) = 0.01$$

$$\therefore P\left(\frac{1}{5.67} < X < 2.85\right) = 1 - 0.05 - 0.01$$

$= 0.94$

6 **b** $H_0 : \mu_B = \mu_A + 150; \quad H_1 : \mu_B > \mu_A + 150$

C.R.: $t_{22}(0.05) > 1.717$

$$S_p^2 = \frac{10 \times 54.0 + 12 \times 21.1\dot{6}}{22} = 36.0909$$

$$t = \frac{755 - 600 - 150}{\sqrt{36.0909...\left(\frac{1}{11} + \frac{1}{13}\right)}} = 2.03157$$

Since 2.03... is in the critical region we reject H_0 and conclude that the mean weight of cauliflowers from B exceeds that from A by at least 50 g.

c Samples from normal populations
Equal variances
Independent samples

7 a $P(X > 19.023) = 0.025$
$P(X > 2.088) = 0.990$
$P(2.088 < X < 19.023) = 0.990 - 0.025$
$= 0.965$

b Upper critical value of $F_{12,5} = 4.68$

Lower critical value of $F_{12,5} = \frac{1}{F_{5,12}}$

$= \frac{1}{3.11}$

$= 0.3215...$

8 a d = coursework – written: 4, −3, −3,4, 6, 3, −4, 17, 7, 7

$\bar{d} = \frac{38}{10} = 3.8,\ s_d^2 = \frac{498 - 10\bar{d}^2}{9} = 39.2\dot{8}$

test statistic: $t = \frac{3.8}{\frac{s_d}{\sqrt{10}}} = 1.917...$

$H_0 : \mu_d = 0, \quad H_1 : \mu_d > 0$

$t_9(5\%)$ c.v. is 1.833

$\therefore$ significant – there is evidence coursework marks are higher.

b The difference between the marks follows a normal distribution.

9 D = dry–wet $\quad H_0 : \mu_D = 0, \quad H_1 : \mu_D \neq 0$

d: 0.6, −1, −1.9, −1.4, −1.3, 0.5, −1.6, −0.6, −1.8

d: $-\frac{8.5}{9} = -0.9\dot{4},\ s_d^2 = \frac{15.03 - 9 \times (\bar{d})^2}{8} = 0.87527...$

$t = \frac{-0.9\dot{4}}{\frac{s_d}{\sqrt{9}}} =$ awrt -3.03

t_8 two-tailed 1% critical value = 3.355

Not significant – insufficient evidence of a difference between mean strength.

10 a i $H_0 : \sigma_C^2 = \sigma_N^2, \quad H_1 : \sigma_C^2 > \sigma_N^2$

$\frac{s_C^2}{s_N^2} = \frac{5.7^2}{3.5^2} = 2.652...;$

$F_{8,9}(5\%)$ critical value = 3.23

Not significant so do not reject H_0. There is insufficient evidence that variance using conventional method is greater.

ii $H_0 : \mu_N = \mu_C, \quad H_1 : \mu_N > \mu_C$

$s^2 = \frac{8 \times 5.7^2 + 9 \times 3.5^2}{17} = \frac{370.17}{17} = 21.774...$

Test statistic $t = \frac{82.3 - 78.2}{\sqrt{21.774...\frac{1}{9} + \frac{1}{10}}} = 1.9122...$

$t_{17}(5\%)$ one-tailed critical value = 1.740

Significant – reject H_0

There is evidence that new style leads to an increase in mean.

b Assumed population of marks obtained were normally distributed.

c Unbiased estimate of common variance is s^2 in **ii**

$7.564 < \frac{17s^2}{\sigma^2} < 30.191$

$\sigma^2 > \frac{17 \times 21.774...}{30.191} = 12.3$ (1 d.p.)

$\sigma^2 < \frac{17 \times 21.774...}{7.564} = 48.9$ (1 d.p.)

CI on σ^2 is (12.3, 48.9)

11 a Confidence interval is given by

$\bar{x} \pm t_{19} \times \frac{s}{\sqrt{n}}$

i.e.: $207.1 \pm 2.539 \times \sqrt{\frac{3.2}{20}}$

i.e.: 207.1 ± 1.0156

i.e.: (206.08..., 208.1156)

b $s_G^2 = \frac{418\,785.4 - \frac{2046.2^2}{10}}{9}$

$s_G^2 = 10.217\dot{3}$

$\bar{x}_G = \frac{2046.2}{10} = 204.62$

$s_p^2 = \frac{19 \times 3.2 + 9 \times 10.217\dot{3}}{28}$

$= 5.45557...$

Confidence interval is given by

$\bar{x}_B - \bar{x}_G \pm t_{28} \times \sqrt{5.45557\left(\frac{1}{20} + \frac{1}{10}\right)}$

i.e.: $(207.1 - 204.62) \pm 1.701\sqrt{5.45557\left(\frac{1}{20} + \frac{1}{10}\right)}$

i.e.: 2.48 ± 1.53875

i.e.: (0.94125, 4.0187)

12 a $\left(\bar{x} = \frac{466}{4} = 116.5\right)\ s_x^2 = \frac{54\,386 - 4\bar{x}^2}{3} = 32.\dot{3}$ or $\frac{97}{3}$

$0.216 < \frac{35x^2}{\sigma^2} < 9.348$

$10.376... < \sigma^2 < 449.07...$

b $H_0 : \sigma_H^2 = \sigma_S^2 \quad H_1 : \sigma_H^2 > \sigma_S^2$

$\frac{s_H^2}{s_S^2} = \frac{318.8}{32.\dot{3}} = 9.859...$

$F_{6,3}$(1% c.v.) = 27.91

9.85 < 27.91, insufficient evidence of an increase in variance

13 a $\left.\begin{matrix} H_0 : \mu_d = 0 \\ H_1 : \mu_d > 0 \end{matrix}\right\}$ where d = without solar heating − with solar heating

d = 6, −3, 7, −2, −8, 6, 5, 11,5

$\bar{d} = 3$

$s_d = 6$

$n_d = 9$

t test statistic $= \frac{(3.0)}{\left(\frac{6}{\sqrt{9}}\right)}$

t.s. = 1.5

critical value = $t_8(5\%) = 1.860$

so critical region: $t > 1.860$

test statistic not in critical region so accept H_0.

Conclude there is insufficient evidence that solar heating reduces mean weekly fuel consumption.

b The differences are normally distributed.

14 a $H_1 : \sigma_A{}^2 = \sigma_B{}^2$, $H_0 : \sigma_A{}^2 \neq \sigma_B{}^2$
$S_A{}^2 = 22.5 \quad S_B{}^2 = 21.6$

$\frac{S_1{}^2}{S_2{}^2} = 1.04$

$F_{(8,6)} = 4.15$
$1.04 < 4.15$ do not reject H_0: The variances are the same.

b Assume the samples are selected at random (independent)

c $s_p{}^2 = \frac{8(22.5) + 6(21.62)}{14} = 22.12$

$H_0 : \mu_A = \mu_B, \quad H_1 : \mu_A \neq \mu_B$

$t = \frac{40.667 - 39.57}{\sqrt{22.12}\sqrt{\frac{1}{9} + \frac{1}{7}}}$
$= 0.462$
Critical value $= t_{14}(2.5\%) = 2.145$
$0.462 < 2.145$ No evidence to reject H_0.
The means are the same.

d Music has no effect on performance.

15 a $H_0 : \sigma_R{}^2 = \sigma_E{}^2 \quad H_1 : \sigma_R{}^2 \neq \sigma_E{}^2$

$F_{6,12}(5\%)_{1\text{ tail}}$ c.v. $= 3.00$, $\frac{s_E{}^2}{s_R{}^2} = \frac{35.79}{14.48} = 2.4716...$

Not significant so do not reject H_0.
Insufficient evidence to suspect $\sigma_R{}^2 \neq \sigma_E{}^2$

b $H_0 : \mu_R = \mu_E, \quad H_1 : \mu_R \neq \mu_E$

$s^2 = \frac{6 \times 35.79 + 12 \times 14.48}{18} = 21.58\dot{3}$

$t = \frac{32.31 - 28.43}{s\sqrt{\frac{1}{13} + \frac{1}{7}}} = 1.78146...$

$t_{18}(5\%)_{2\text{ tail}}$ c.v. $= 2.101$
$\therefore$ Not significant.
Insufficient evidence of difference in mean performance.

c Test in **b** requires $\sigma_1{}^2 = \sigma_2{}^2$

d e.g. same: type of driving
roads and journey length
weather
driver

16 a $H_0 : \sigma_A{}^2 = \sigma_B{}^2 \quad H_1 : \sigma_A{}^2 \neq \sigma_B{}^2$
critical value $F_{24,25} = 1.96$

or $\frac{1}{F_{24,25}} = 0.510$

$\frac{s_B{}^2}{s_A{}^2} = 2.10$

or $\frac{s_A{}^2}{s_B{}^2} = 0.476$

Since 2.10 (or 0.476) is in the critical region so we reject H_0 and conclude there is evidence that the two variances are different.

b The populations of pebble lengths are normal.

Exam practice paper

2 $H_0 : \sigma_m{}^2 = \sigma_s{}^2 \quad H_1 : \sigma_m{}^2 > \sigma_s{}^2$

From calculator $s_s{}^2 = \frac{66\,506 - \frac{576^2}{5}}{4} = 37.7$

$F = \frac{240.3}{37.7} = 6.374...$

$F_{5,4}$ 1% significance level critical value is 6.26
$6.374... > 6.26$ so test is significant, reject H_0
There is evidence that the weights of apples from the market stall are more varied.

3 a $H_0 : \sigma^2 = 11.16 \quad H_1 : \sigma^2 > 11.16$
1% critical value from χ^2_{11} is 24.725

$\frac{11S^2}{11.16} > 24.725$

So CR for S^2 is $S^2 > 25.0846... = 25.085$ (3 d.p.)

b P(Type II error) $= \text{P}(S^2 < 25.085 \mid \sigma^2 = 49.45)$

Now $\frac{(n-1)S^2}{\sigma^2} \sim \chi^2_{n-1}$

So P(Type II error) $= \text{P}\left(\chi^2_{11} < \frac{11 \times 25.085}{49.45}\right)$
$= \text{P}(\chi^2_{11} < 5.580)$
$= 1 - 0.90$
$= 0.10$

4 a Let D = distance with additive − distance without additive
d: 3, −1, 2, 6, −5, 5, 6

$\bar{d} = \frac{16}{7} = 2.2857... \quad s_d = \sqrt{\frac{136 - \frac{16^2}{7}}{6}} = 4.07...$

$H_0 : \mu_D = 0, \quad H_1 : \mu_D > 0$

$t = \frac{2.285...\ 2\ 0}{\frac{4.07}{\sqrt{7}}} = 1.485...$

t_6 (10%) critical value $= 1.440$
The test is significant so there is evidence to support the manufacturer's claim.

b Assumed that the differences between mileages are normally distributed.

5 a Let $\sigma_m{}^2$ be variance with music
$H_0 : \sigma^2 = \sigma_m{}^2 \quad H_1 : \sigma^2 \neq \sigma_m{}^2$

$F = \frac{6.84^2}{5.29^2} = 1.671...$

$F_{12,9}$ critical value $= 3.07$
So the test is not significant – the variances can be assumed equal.

b Let μ_m be mean with music
$H_0 : \mu = \mu_m, \quad H_1 : \mu \neq \mu_m$

$s_p{}^2 = \frac{9 \times 5.29^2 + 12 \times 6.84^2}{10 + 13 - 2} = 38.72...$

So $t = \frac{23.36 - 19.96 - 0}{\sqrt{38.72...} \times \sqrt{\frac{1}{10} + \frac{1}{13}}} = 1.298...$

t_{21} 5% two-tail c.v. is 2.080
Test is not significant – there is insufficient evidence of a difference in mean heights. No evidence to support the idea of playing music to increase average height.

c The test in part **b** requires that both the variances are equal.
The test in **a** established that this was reasonable.

6 a $\bar{x} = \frac{1289}{6} = 214.8... \quad s_d = \sqrt{\frac{277\,259 - 6\bar{x}^2}{5}} = 8.23...$

i 95% CI for μ is

$\bar{x} \pm 2.571 \times \frac{s_d}{\sqrt{6}} = 214.8... \pm 2.571 \times \frac{8.23}{\sqrt{6}}$
$= (206.19..., 223.47...)$

ii Using $\frac{5s_d^2}{\sigma^2} \sim \chi_5^2$

From tables $P(\chi_5^2 < 0.831) = 0.025$

and $P(\chi_5^2 > 12.832) = 0.025$

$26.405\ldots \frac{5s_d^2}{12.832} < \sigma^2 < \frac{5s_d^2}{0.831} = 407.74\ldots$

95% CI for σ is (5.14, 20.2)

b Let S = span of an adult male's hand

$P(S > 230) = P\left(Z > \frac{230 - \mu}{\sigma}\right)$

For a maximum value you need largest μ and largest σ.

i.e. $P\left(Z > \frac{230 - 223.47\ldots}{20.1925\ldots}\right) = P(Z > 0.323\ldots)$

$= 1 - 0.6255$
$= 0.3745$

So the largest proportion is 0.37 (2 s.f.)

7 a $E(X^n) = \int_0^t x^n \times \frac{1}{t}\,dx$

$= \left[\frac{x^{n+1}}{t(n+1)}\right]_0^t = \frac{t^{n+1}}{t(n+1)} = \frac{t^n}{n+1}$

d $\text{Var}(X^3) = E(X^6) - [E(X^3)]^2$

$= \frac{t^6}{7} - \left(\frac{t^3}{4}\right)^2 = \frac{9t^2}{112}$

$\text{Var}(S) = 4\text{Var}(X^3) + \text{Var}(Y^3) + \text{Var}(Z^3)$

$= (4 + 1 + 1) \times \frac{9t^6}{112} = \frac{27t^6}{56}$

e $E(T) = k \times \frac{3t^3}{4}$

So $k = \frac{4}{3}$

f $\text{Var}(T) = k^2\left(3 \times \frac{9t^6}{112}\right) = \frac{3t^6}{7}$

g Since $\frac{3t^6}{7} = \frac{24t^6}{56} < \frac{27t^6}{56}$ T is the better estimate

h Using T the estimate is: $\frac{4}{3} \times (1^3 + 3^3 + 2^3) = 48$

Index